BALDY'S BOOK

Adrian Sudbury was a web journalist on The Huddersfield Daily Examiner when he was diagnosed with two forms of leukaemia in November, 2006. According to medical literature, he was the only person in the world to have this condition. Adrian decided to share his experiences of the disease and his treatment in an online diary - Baldy's Blog. His informed and informal style won a host of national and international awards and a raft of followers from across the world, christened - with a typical love of alliteration - Adrian's Army. His condition was confirmed as terminal in May, 2008. Adrian then launched a high profile media campaign to raise awareness about bone marrow donation, one that took him all the way to Downing Street. As a result of his efforts, all sixth form students will hopefully soon undergo a one hour tutorial explaining the benefits of signing up to a bone marrow donor register. The National Blood Donor Service and Anthony Nolan Trust estimate donor enquiries doubled during the 'Sign Up for Sudders' campaign. Adrian died, aged 27, in August, 2008.

Baldy's Book is published by :

Trinity Mirror NW²

Trinity Mirror North West & North Wales
PO Box 48
Old Hall Street,
Liverpool L69 3EB

Business Development Director:
Mark Dickinson

Business Development Executive Editor:
Ken Rogers

Editor:
Roy Wright

Book and Cover Design:
Charlie Hearnshaw

ISBN 978-1-905266-96-8

 ## ADRIAN SUDBURY
JUNE 2008

I know what you're thinking - "Oh God, not another cancer book" - and quite frankly you'd be right. I am a journalist and as any decent journalist will tell you we are not good writers. In fact the very best in our trade can barely screw a sentence together but we do excel at digging out tales, getting feet in doors and sniffing out wrong-doing at all levels of society.

When I got ill it seemed like everyone was saying, 'You should write about it - why not write a blog?' Blogs eh? Aren't they one of those things everyone writes these days, especially when they get ill, that contain fascinating revelations about how many apples they have eaten that day or whether or not they were able to tie their shoe laces.

Blogs are for nerds and, with a few exceptions, are generally shite.

Anyway, not wanting to conform to the usual hypocrisy demonstrated in today's media, I realised that treatment for leukaemia was going to take at least six months away from my reporting life. It was a job I loved and, when I wasn't vomiting from chemotherapy or wrestling with extreme illness, I realised I was going to have contributed nothing for at least half a year.

A blog it was then.

Joking aside, I have to say it was one of the best decisions I ever made during my treatment. I knew that with the new multimedia equipment at the office and a burgeoning knowledge of the internet, there was a great opportunity to do something unique with this tiny Huddersfield Examiner project.

If I had been fit enough to transform this blog into a book then I would have liked to include the history of leukaemia and some of the early experiments. It's not been discovered for as long as people think.

I also had this idea that the blog would continue and I could keep in touch with book readers via the blog.

Oh well, regular cancer book it is, let's see how many copies get pulped.

GORDON BROWN
PRIME MINISTER

I n May 2008, Adrian Sudbury received the news he dreaded: the treatment he had received for leukaemia had failed. He had just weeks to live, with no realistic hope of a cure.

Most of us cannot imagine even receiving that news, let alone how we would deal with it.

But I think all of us would hope to react like Adrian.

Where it would be all too natural to feel frightened, angry or helpless, Adrian's response was full of courage, humour and an unbreakable resolve.

The resolve to do everything until his last breath to help and inspire others, and give hope to the 7,000 people in Britain waiting for bone marrow transplants.

In the space of a few weeks, he has done years' worth of work to raise awareness of the need for bone marrow donors.

His campaign has already attracted thousands of supporters, and his memory will continue to inspire its action for years to come.

When I met Adrian in the House of Commons shortly after his terminal illness was confirmed, he made me promise that the Government would do more to encourage bone marrow donation, particularly by educating young people about the procedure in our schools and colleges, and dispelling the common myths.

And we will.

But in that meeting, I did not see a dying man.

I saw someone who epitomised a life lived to the full, determined to make the most of every moment and determined to make a real difference.

And as always, totally selfless: more concerned about how his family and friends were feeling than about himself.

Even as Adrian's health declined sharply, and he became a shadow of the energetic, football-playing, brilliant young journalist his friends knew, his spirit was undimmed. And just as he fought bravely for two years against the most virulent form of leukaemia, he fought to carry on his dying work as long as possible.

He was a true hero: a true inspiration not just to others suffering from terminal illness, but to every one of us.

My father told me when I was young that everyone has the chance to make their mark on this world, whether for good or bad.

Adrian Sudbury has left his mark for good.

SLY BAILEY
CHIEF EXECUTIVE,
TRINITY MIRROR PLC

Once in a while somebody comes along who makes such an impression on you that you know you will never forget them. Somebody who makes you sit up and take notice, gives you a fresh perspective and changes your outlook on life.

Somebody who, when faced with tremendous adversity, shows such strength, courage and good humour that you can't help but be both humbled and inspired.

Adrian Sudbury was one of those rare people.

Adrian joined us at Trinity Mirror in 2003 as a keen, young reporter covering news and features for the Express and Chronicle in Huddersfield.

By 2006 he had been promoted to the role of digital journalist with the Huddersfield Examiner but soon after taking up his new position he was diagnosed with leukaemia.

It's at this point that Adrian's true colours shone through and when it became clear that he was more than just a cracking young journalist.

Adrian's response was to face his illness head on. He responded to it in the best way he knew how: he wrote about it. A journalist to the core. And what a brilliant journalist he was.

Adrian's blog chronicling his brave daily battle with leukaemia won countless awards and garnered huge international acclaim. But more important than this, Adrian's openness, honesty and dignity in chronicling the ups and downs of his progress provided comfort to fellow sufferers and attracted friends and admirers the world over.

Ever the pragmatist, Adrian then led a magnificent campaign to persuade the Government to introduce education about bone marrow donation into schools and colleges, a crusade which took him all the way to 10 Downing Street.

This collection of Adrian's blogs is a document of two years in the life of a remarkable young man. A young man of tremendous character whose memory will continue to inspire us, and the lives of everyone he touched along the way.

We will never forget him.

KALI MOUNTFORD
MP, COLNE VALLEY

Some people reading this will have never met Adrian but must feel you know him from his blog, believe me he was an even more incredible guy than you think. Of course he was brave and courageous and funny but his blog doesn't really do justice to his fantastic zest for life which sings out of his every pore.

Sometimes you meet people in life who can make a difference and Adrian was one of those people.

I first met Adrian when he started out as a most junior reporter with the Colne Valley Chronicle. He was always engaging and funny and I soon found myself agreeing to letting him spend the day with me in the House of Commons. He even found his way into the Treasury. I introduced him to senior ministers including Des Browne who I worked for at the time and who was Chief Secretary to the Treasury. Adrian was itching to see Gordon Brown but Gordon gets up too early for us mere mortals and had flown the nest. So, Adrian had to content himself with a cup of coffee with the treasury press officer. He quizzed me about ID cards, I was speaking on the bill committee at the time and not wasting any copy managed to get at least three stories out of his trip to London.

I'm not sure what Adrian made of the day as I tried to introduce him to as many people as possible. I remember laughing all day and then reading a double page spread which ended with the words… 'and I still don't know what an MP does'.

Our most recent work together brought him closer than ever to my job so I wonder if Adrian ever did find out what I do?

Well I know what he did. He brought a joy to the campaign, a spring to our step, a purpose to each day, an inspiration to each of us, a memory to treasure. Thank you for all of it.

STEVE MCEWAN
CHIEF EXECUTIVE OF THE
ANTHONY NOLAN TRUST

Adrian was an inspirational individual. I met him after he had his transplant and he was incredibly keen to help the charity in getting its message across.

The fact that he was still campaigning right up to his final weeks means our admiration for the man is extraordinary. I have had a number of responses from people who have been on Adrian's blog.

I think anyone who reads that blog would know what an amazing story he has told. His message and the way he wrote was special.

It sometimes does take an emotional push to get people to join the register. It may be that you tag along with a friend to a clinic or maybe you join because a relative needs a transplant.

If you are trying to talk in abstract terms about bone marrow and registers it is not the same as seeing someone make a personal push like Adrian did.

It's not always easy for people to understand what we do. Sometimes it takes a donor or patient to recruit a donor. You do need to have that opportunity to sit down with someone or hear someone's story to know what's involved.

If schools and colleges made pupils aware of what bone marrow donation involved, then as adults they may be more likely to become donors.

We would totally accept that the message of what being a donor means should be got across at a younger age.

That's why the Government backing for the campaign will be helpful. It is not the Government that recruits donors; it's people. But its support is important to facilitate what we are trying to achieve.

Vic Derbyshire
Radio Five
Live Presenter

Five Live listeners don't suffer fools; they are some of the most critical people I've come across. They're also some of the most compassionate and selfless people I've ever had the privilege of getting to know. They adored Adrian Sudbury - and it wasn't because he was dying. If I had to analyse why I'd say it's because he was normal. In my family being described as 'normal' is one of the greatest compliments you can bestow. Adrian was frank, pragmatic, patient, lacking in self pity - and living through abnormal times. Our listeners heard him explain his illness, his setbacks, and his mission to ensure a talk on bone marrow, organ and blood donation was included in the national curriculum. They spontaneously rang in to support him, to give him their love and ask how they could help. He told them about his blog, his online petition and how they could sign up to the register. They wanted to tell him he was inspirational and wish him all the best. A man called Jeff phoned in from Southampton, a Portsmouth supporter, and offered Adrian his FA Cup final ticket - in case he'd never been and wanted to experience it just once. (Adrian was taken aback by the kindness but said Jeff should go; Portsmouth won). Others offered to sign the petition, more said they would register as a donor - it was a "no brainer".

Adrian had an unassuming way of talking that drew you towards him. When he first spoke on the radio I wanted to absorb every word he was saying to me about his illness. He was compelling. You think stupid thoughts: how can this horrible thing be happening to a nice guy like this? How can he be so composed about the crap life is throwing at him? And, selfishly, why aren't I more like him?

Adrian was a guest on the programme only three times - he made a lasting impression. It's because he was normal.

ROY WRIGHT
EDITOR, HUDDERSFIELD
DAILY EXAMINER

Bloggers only know Adrian's beanie hat and big smiley face. They only know the young man facing turmoil with grace, courage and humour. But there used to be another Sudders.

When I met Adrian in 2004, he was a carefree, tall, skinny journalist on our weekly paper… and possibly the best mannered reporter I've ever met (which isn't necessarily saying much).

He was a mother's dream. I used to admire his phone manner - well-spoken, polite but to the point - and wondered why all our reporters could never manage that.

One day Adrian came out in a cold sweat! He'd made a mistake in the copy. He then rang everyone in the story individually and apologised.

And while he was talented, it was never in an obvious way.

But only now re-reading all his blogs does it become clear what a fine writer he was. Adrian was diligent and honest and nuts about anything scientific. He once offered to cover any science stories for the daily paper - in his own time. Again another first.

He moved up to take charge of our website despite competition from more senior candidates. But he was the best candidate. He talked about blogs and reader interactivity in a knowledgeable and informed way while I nodded slowly.

We first discussed a blog shortly after he fell ill. He hadn't been in the role long and - knowing Adrian - I suspect he felt a bit guilty about being off work. And being an editor, I was happy to exploit this.

If Adrian had still been around to update our website today, he wouldn't have met Gordon Brown, nor won four major journalism awards. Though we'd all swap one for the other.

But from extraordinary circumstances come extraordinary deeds. Adrian was not destined for a normal life. Nor was he going to accept his illness, withdraw into his shell and grow bitter.

He launched the campaign for better education about bone marrow donation.

It deserves to succeed and if it does will save lives. As simple as that. There can be no more fitting legacy for Sudders.

Adrian Sudbury was about the nicest person I've known in journalism. Trouble is I didn't know him for long enough.

Editor's Note

Almost all the blog comments have been edited out; if not, the book would be too big to fit on any bookshelf... but no less interesting. However it probably needs some explanation. And apologies to any regular bloggers who have been missed. I have used only first names to give an element of anonymity. It would have taken too long to trace everyone to ask their permission. Adrian attracted a huge range of regular readers from across the world and many had health problems in their close family. In fairness to them I've tried to leave their comments out. Adrian's calm, chatty but informative writing helped many understand what leukaemia sufferers - and cancer patients in general - go through. But it was no one-way thing. Adrian received huge support back and made many genuine friends through the blog. Reading them again for this book, I could feel things coming together, Adrian's Army gaining momentum. "One big family" was how one regular described it, which seems about right. So a big thank you to anyone who 'blogged' Baldy. You don't need me to tell you what it meant to him. But most of all thank you Adrian.

HOW IT ALL BEGAN

March 28, 2007

"How long would I have lived if I hadn't driven myself into hospital?" I asked.

"Maybe about another two or three weeks, it's hard to tell," my consultant replied.

That revelation was like a slap in the face. Everything else that was swirling around my mind; being a cancer patient, the length of time I would be in hospital, chemotherapy and its awful side effects, the fear of not achieving remission, all collapsed into a single moment of clarity - there was no choice but to start treatment.

That meeting took place in early December between my consultant, girlfriend Poppy, my parents and sister.

On reflection the early days were overwhelming. I was a fit and healthy 25-year-old, who doesn't smoke, has no history of cancer in the family and has a job I like.

It was hard to understand why all this was happening and to comprehend the difficult times that lay ahead.

But now, after having completed my second cycle of chemotherapy, I am determined to get over this disease and reclaim my normal life as quickly as possible.

As part of this I thought writing a series of blogs for www.examiner.co.uk would help me keep in touch with the 'real world' that exists outside my ward.

But having talked to many people about leukaemia, and looking back on my own thoughts after being initially diagnosed, I think few know very little about the disease and the treatments that are associated with it.

In the following weekly blogs I thought I would share my experiences with you but also explain what leukaemia is, what chemotherapy is and how it works. I don't know why but I always imagined that some sort of machine is involved - it isn't by the way.

Most importantly I want to stress that these accounts are not all, 'Boo-hoo I've got leukaemia.' Despite many difficult times, unpleasant reactions to treatments and extreme illness, there have also been plenty of uplifting and genuinely funny moments.

Moreover, I'm now exceedingly confident I'm going to get out of this situation, get back to my girlfriend, family and, of course, the mighty Examiner.

Lastly I have a confession to make: with a few exceptions I generally loathe blogs. Who's really interested in a pet cat, someone buying new shoes or top tips on how to plant potatoes?

So, with that said, I just hope my blogs don't fall into the unacceptable category of really bloody boring.

COMMENTS (45)

I was gutted to hear you were ill and I'm really chuffed for you that you're making good progress. *Jenny*

Good luck Sudders. I'm sure your positive attitude will help you pull through. Best wishes to all your family and Poppy too. Keep the blogs coming can't wait for the next one. *Sam*

Hat goes on, hat goes off, hat goes on, hat goes off... love it. Don't go thinking this gets you out of cleaning the bathroom though because it doesn't. *Poppy*

The blog is looking good and so is your hair do. All the best from everyone down in the Liverpool office. Look after yourself matey. *Liam*

Good to see you doing some work at last! Now get yourself well and get yourself back to Queen Street South and the sooner the better. *John Griffith*

Football on Thursdays are not the same without you and your skills. *Steve*

HOW IT ALL BEGAN (PART 2)
March 30, 2007

I've never been like Geoff Capes but before all this I was fit and healthy.

Each week last summer I was running 5km, swimming, doing boxing training and playing 5-a-side with lads from the Examiner down at Soccer City in Waterloo. I don't smoke or drink (excessively) and I still find it hard to understand how quickly I became so seriously ill.

Truth be told, I had been suffering slightly for the previous 18 months. I seemed to pick up colds and chest infections remarkably easily and then they would stay around for three weeks, whereas previously they would have cleared up much more quickly.

By October last year I had stopped all sport because of a mysterious pain deep in my right thigh. It was very uncomfortable and was not getting better like a pull or a strain tends to. I asked a physiotherapist to have a look and she could not find anything wrong with it. More on this pain later.

On a more positive note in that same month I was promoted from regular reporter to 'digital journalist'. This effectively meant I would be editing and putting news onto this new site.

Being a bit rubbish at computers I was sent over to our sister paper, the Liverpool Echo, for a week long course on how to operate the system.

During that week it's fair to say I deteriorated. I remember one night following work I went to meet an old friend in a bar for a drink. I had one pint, promptly vomited, made my apologies and headed back to my hotel where I slipped into a cold sleep.

A virulent cough and cold had taken their grip and I was finding it harder to concentrate on what I was doing. I was also starting to suffer from fatigue - I was shattered from mid-afternoon onwards.

I finished the course and gratefully headed home thinking a restful weekend would see me right and return to work full of vim and vigour.

It didn't. The new site was launched and along with my video colleague, we had two really successful days operating the new site, updating it with fresh material throughout the day.

In fact things were going so well I decided to ask for some time off to get better. I went to the Doctors and was told to take a week off work. I did this but it wasn't helping. The fatigue was getting ridiculous. I can remember washing the pots one day and having to go for a nap half way through.

I tried to give work one more go the following week but it was no good. Just walking up the stairs was exhausting. I had become really pale and all my colleagues said I should go home.

After half a day, and a 15 minute kip in the medical room, I did just that. I went back to the Doctors where I was given the following advice, "Drink a cup of warm lemon juice and honey".

The next day, with no idea what else to do, I got in my car and drove myself to the A&E at Sheffield's Northern General - I have been in hospital ever since.

COMMENTS (6)

My first thought was why is Telly Savalas writing a blog? You are the most upbeat man I've ever had the pleasure to meet - you make me feel sick! In short a really nice, fun loving and superb individual who is genuinely one of the nicest people I've ever had the pleasure to meet. Enough fawning over the ill man! *Andrew Jackson*

Adrian is a truly remarkable young man. We are writing this to let him know that we are hopefully bringing 'Big Grama' into the 21st century by getting her to subscribe to his blog. *Uncle Brian and Aunty Lucy*

DIAGNOSIS
April 2, 2007 12pm

It might sound strange but in some ways I was relieved when it became clear leukaemia was responsible for my symptoms.

When I was ill I did the one thing I promised myself I would never do - use the internet to diagnose what was wrong.

I had entered all my symptoms and, according to the world wide web, I had ME. In some respects I found the prospect of this condition even more distressing.

Anyway, in A&E the doctors quickly established that my heart and other major organs were OK with the exception of a considerably enlarged spleen and liver.

Admittedly I found this pretty alarming.

More armfuls of blood were taken leaving my veins like sieves, not a particularly enjoyable experience for someone who is a bit squeamish.

I was then transferred to the haematology ward at Sheffield's Royal Hallamshire Hospital.

Typically leukaemia is relatively easy to diagnose, it can often be done within 24 hours, but my precise problem remained difficult for the doctors to get a handle on.

Looking back it must have been about three weeks before they were ready to begin treatment, in the meantime my illness was monitored and I received my first blood transfusions.

This is a strange experience. Imagine someone else's blood flowing slowly towards your arm. You can see the red getting ever closer and wonder what it's going to feel like, whose blood it is and reflect on how weird the whole concept is.

But then after the first bag is in you just feel so much better that you never have those feelings again - you just want more!

Those early weeks were difficult. Not knowing what is wrong with you is sometimes far worse than knowing the challenges you face.

I can remember walking around the ward and seeing lots of people with the distinctive hair loss that follows chemotherapy. I also saw lots of very ill patients. I had not really thought about leukaemia until I arrived on the ward.

On my strolls around, closer inspection revealed that paintings on the walls were all in memory of loved ones. Someone had also placed a copy of Psalm 23, the 'walk through the valley of the shadow of death' one, on one of the sides of the corridors.

I slowly realised that I could be in a pretty difficult situation.

Then, when one of the doctors was called away, I peered into the tray that had been left behind. There were several cards which had come back from blood test results. I nervously flicked through them. Each in turn simply said 'Leukaemia?'

Now I was bricking it.

Then the diagnosis finally came; I had Acute Myeloid Leukaemia (AML).

COMMENTS (5)

You don't really know me but we have met a couple of times - I'm a friend of Richard Porritt's (I get through it) and I've bumped into you a few times. I started running - for fun would you believe - a year and a bit ago and have been thinking about entering some sort of event. Anyway, I've signed up for one (in Leeds) and because of reading this blog I've decided to raise money for a Leukaemia charity. I have no idea if I'll raise enough money to actually make a true contribution - but we'll see. *Gavin, Huddersfield*

Long time no see my friend. Ant told me about your blog, so I thought I'd have a little gander and leave ya a comment. It's a good read so far. Two bits stand out for me. Like you said the transfusion must have been weird, but I did read somewhere that Keith Richards has a blood transfusion every year and pays thousands for it so you know, you got it free. You gotta look on the upside!! And the bit about the warm lemon juice and honey!! Flipping useless. The beautiful British NHS system lives on. *Ryan*

REACTION
April 4, 2007

Leukaemia is an emotive word. Like cancer it is so emotionally charged that you hope its diagnosis is something you never have to tell your girlfriend or parents.

I think we were all braced for the news but that doesn't necessarily make it any easier. It really upset my parents. One image that will always stay with me is seeing in my mum and dad's bedroom the kettle and tea pot, a clear sign of many sleepless nights worrying.

Personally it was difficult but I knew I could focus my thoughts on fighting the disease and striving to cope with the treatment.

For my girlfriend, family and friends, all they can do is support me and that is it. Something I have learnt is that in many ways it is more difficult for people around you who are unable to do anything. I would hate it if it was one of them lying here rather than me. All I have to do is lie back and let the medical team pour chemicals into me.

Poppy, my girlfriend, works full time as an engineer then comes to the hospital to see me for two hours at night. She would never dream of not visiting but it's exhausting for her.

This might sound strange but I found the risk of being rendered infertile far more difficult to cope with than dying. Chemotherapy used to treat Acute Myeloid Leukaemia is strong stuff. As well as hair loss there is also a very high risk of being left permanently sterile.

Having a family is something that has always been very important to me, and my girlfriend, so this news was devastating. I was so upset that I had to see a counsellor. I haven't cried since my grandma's funeral but I couldn't stop the tears streaming out.

Thankfully talking about my worries really helped me.

There was so much to take in - including a trip to the fertility wing to give a sample.

Trust me, I was so ill at this stage that it was the last thing I wanted to do. Because I was poorly I had to be pushed over to the department in a wheel chair by one of the nurses. Then I was handed my pot.

After it was all over I turned to the nurse and said: "Well this is socially awkward." She just smiled and told me that it's no big deal for them. A sense of normality made the whole situation feel far less degrading.

When I returned to my bed there was a package waiting for me. I opened it to find a portable DVD player from my friends at work and the lads I played football with. That present would turn out to be a real Godsend. The reaction of all my friends was like this, just incredible, and I would like to say how grateful I am for everything they have done for me.

COMMENTS (14)

It takes pure courage to make any sense of what you're going through and even more guts to share it. I have worked alongside cancer patients for 17 years and believe me you have reminded me what wonderful and remarkable people you get to know. You clearly have zillions of people rooting for you - add me to the list. *Meriel*

When Ad first went into hospital, I did too, but for a much more mundane broken leg. And every time that I rang from my sofa to his hospital bed, the first thing Ad would ask was 'How is your leg?' And I think that just sums him up. *Helen*

WHAT IS LEUKAEMIA?
April 10, 2007

Despite my bone marrow being more dysfunctional than a group of ASBO kids who have recently guzzled ready meals aplenty, washed down with flagons of pop, I have to say I have a new found respect for this incredible tissue. Your marrow is responsible for producing the following cells of the blood:
- Red blood cells which carry oxygen around the body.
- Platelets which stop you from bleeding to death if cut.
- White blood cells which fight off bacterial infections.

In an adult, in order to sustain the necessary levels of blood cells, the marrow works at a phenomenal rate. It has to produce around 3 million red blood cells and 120,000 white blood cells - every second!

When this immaculate system is impaired serious problems occur.

Leukaemia is essentially a cancer of the blood. There are many different types and sub-groups of which Acute Myeloid Leukaemia (AML) is one. It's pretty serious but also the most common form of the disease in adults.

The majority of cells in the body are programmed to die at a certain point. In cancer this controlled cell death is overridden and the cells proliferate uncontrollably. And so it is with AML. At some point something went wrong in my marrow and cells began to divide without restraint.

In reality, the situation is much more complex but it was explained to me like this. Imagine the space inside a bone. If cells in the marrow are proliferating then this will affect the production of all the blood cells. In my case the cells were being 'squeezed out' of the marrow before they were ready. Effectively this meant they were useless.

Regarding my symptoms, leukaemia explained why I was so pale because I had a lack of functioning red blood cells. This also meant I was exhausted as not enough oxygen was being carried around my body. In fact, my consultant said it was like walking around with three bags of blood missing.

It also explained why I was so susceptible to bacterial infections because my white blood cells were not protecting me as they should.

In one of my earlier blogs I described a deep pain in my right thigh that wasn't getting better. It has been suggested this could have been the cancerous cells increasing in number and pushing out onto the bone.

Inevitably the next question is what causes this cancer? The answer unfortunately is not clear. If you don't smoke, have not been exposed to benzene or were not in Hiroshima at the time of the bomb, then it's probably just bad luck. In the beginning it was something I would spend many hours thinking about.

Now I am resigned to the fact that we will never know what triggered it and in some ways I think this is easier to deal with. It means you can't look back at a particular time or situation with bitter regret.

The disease is indiscriminate affecting people of all ages and backgrounds. Around 110,000 people in the UK have a blood cancer and each year it will kill around 11,000.

People tend to think it's a disease that primarily affects children. This isn't the case. Approximately 500 are diagnosed in the UK each year, the bulk are older patients.

Treatment has improved massively since the 1960s and for AML patients between 75 and 80% will achieve remission after several cycles of chemotherapy. However, only around 35% of these patients will never be bothered by the disease again.

I believe the odds are much better for young children with the disease.

COMMENTS (9)

Love the new instalments - science is indeed now accessible to all with handy diagrams and noddy language for us non physiologists (also known as idiots...)! I cannot wait for the transplant explanation so will continue to watch this space. You know I love you (and will love you even more when I have retrieved my iPod from your possession). *Hannah*

TREATING LEUKAEMIA
April 12, 2007

The first weapon in the fight against Acute Myeloid Leukaemia (AML) is chemotherapy. Patients are given a cocktail of chemicals that attack rapidly dividing cells.

But as well as killing off the cancerous cells it also affects other similar cells in the body - hence the undesirable side effects. Hair loss occurs because hair follicles are hit. Strong chemotherapy also wipes out cells that line the gut making it incredibly difficult to eat food and can cause severe diarrhoea. It also inadvertently affects the cells involved in reproduction.

One of the main advances in the treatment of leukaemia is the Hickman line. It is inserted into a vein below the neck and the internal end sits just above the heart. The other end emerges with two little pipes and sits on the outside of your chest.

It's inserted under a local anaesthetic. I wouldn't say it's a particularly pleasant experience but it is totally painless. For the first couple of days it feels a little strange having these two tubes dangling in front of you but you quickly forget about it.

It's very useful because suddenly your daily blood test can be taken from the line, blood can be put in through it, as can antibiotics should you fall ill. Anything put into you goes directly to the heart and is distributed immediately throughout the blood system. The line, therefore, is also great for chemotherapy.

AML patients are normally given four or five cycles of chemotherapy. There are different combinations of the chemicals and the regimes can last between five and ten days.

Bags of the chemicals are placed on drip stands and then you are hooked up to it via your Hickman line. That's all it is. The bags I had lasted between half an hour and four hours.

To begin with I reacted very badly. I would be sick at regular intervals and, due to the fact I am quite loud when vomiting, my three friends in the room would cheer me on in support!

The second problem I experienced during the treatment was that it caused extreme fevers. Again, with spooky regularity, my temperature would begin to soar yet I would feel freezing on the inside. Imagine the coldest you have ever been and no matter how many layers of clothes you put on, or hats you wear, it would make no difference at all.

These phases lasted for around an hour and were horrible. I would be shivering uncontrollably then eventually my body would switch over and it felt like I was roasting. I would typically be sick in between the two stages and then rapidly have to rip off the many layers of clothes I had put on previously.

Interestingly, I learnt that good old, simple paracetamol, is fantastic at controlling these fevers.

As I progressed through my first lot of chemotherapy the nurses tinkered around with a combination of anti-sickness and anti-inflammatory drugs to combat these side-effects. By the last day they had finally cracked it and I felt much better.

The hope is that several different courses of chemotherapy will be enough to wipe out all the cancerous cells and achieve remission. If this isn't the case then a bone marrow transplant may be the only hope.

But just as the first load of chemotherapy was coming to an end I was to receive some more bad news.

COMMENTS (13)

Hey you - how about a cliffhanger! I am loving the blog mate. Even not very bright people like me can understand what's going on, which must be a tribute to your writing skills. *Campers*

I'm not convinced the odds are better for children, I've been in remission from AML for four and a half years now, I'm now 44 The Hickman line looks all too familiar!!! Stay positive and well, you can get through this believe me! *Judith*

It occurred to me that as you drove yourself into hospital in the first place, you may have left your car in the car park. They could be still charging you if you haven't moved it yet. *Andy N*

MORE BAD NEWS
April 17, 2007

The chemotherapy seemed to be going well but then my doctors got a letter from the genetics laboratory.

Prior to treatment a sample of my bone marrow was taken from the back of my pelvis. If you lean forward and put your hands just above your waist, the slight bony lumps either side of the spine, is where they tend to take it from.

This is sent away for thorough genetic analysis. The bad news for me was the tests showed I had a second type of chronic leukaemia.

In an earlier blog I described that my diagnosis took quite some time. This was why. Under the microscope I had indications of both Acute Myeloid Leukaemia (AML) and a chronic type too. At the time, the conclusion was that a chronic leukaemia had evolved into an acute one.

These results showed both were working at the same time.

My consultant, who is a world expert, trawled through all the medical literature and could find no one with the condition. He later got in touch with his global counterparts and heard that there may be five patients with a similar condition in Germany but that nothing had been reported officially.

As such, he said he could no longer offer me an accurate prognosis but was keen to push on with treatment. The concern now was whether the two types of leukaemia were interacting and if so how. The belief was they probably were and that the chronic form, which could have been grumbling on for years, finally triggered the acute outbreak.

The chronic problem, as illustrated below, is occurring further back in the marrow, around the level of one of the stem cells from which the other cells originate.

Chemotherapy may or may not wipe out these earlier cells. Just how much of a problem they were remained to be seen. But the good news was that if the chronic cells were limited in their abnormality then they could be managed with a new drug called Glivec.

This drug has been hugely successful in treating Chronic Myeloid Leukaemia (CML). It works by inhibiting the effects of the mutated cells and seems to be effective for many years.

The plan was to crack on with the chemotherapy, achieve remission and then monitor the chronic problem. If it became an issue then treat with Glivec.

Needless to say being diagnosed with two types of leukaemia was a bit of a blow yet bizarrely my ego was purring at potentially being a sort of 'world first'. If only it had been in something slightly less life threatening.

COMMENTS (6)

Some people's excuses for not coming to my wedding have been quite poor so far. But I think going to the extremes of writing this blog to prove the reasoning for your absence is excessive! However Hannah and I will be thinking of you on the day, probably something along the lines of we wish Adie was here so he could drag Poppy off the dance floor! *Neil*

My partner who I previously left a comment on your blog about is on GLIVEC - apart from a few nasty side effects to start with it is now doing it's job! Thankfully there are signs of a remission taking place. *Jason*

CHRISTMAS AND GETTING ILL
April 19, 2007

One of the hardest things to explain to friends and family is why the treatment of leukaemia requires so much time in hospital.

The reason is the chemotherapy is targeting the bone marrow, wiping out all the cells that shouldn't be there. Unfortunately this results in all the other cells the marrow makes being disrupted.

This means that no more platelets, or white and red blood cells, are produced. On the ward your blood is taken each day and the amounts of each of these cells are recorded. They are known as your counts and you quickly become obsessed with them.

Post-chemotherapy your counts come crashing down. This means regular transfusions of platelets and red blood cells are required.

Sadly your white blood cells cannot be replenished in the same way. The marrow makes a variety of different white blood cells but the ones we're concerned with are called neutrophils. When the counts hit zero it is known as neutropenia. This means your immune system has no bacteria fighting ability.

Counts can take between 10 and 20 days to recover so during this time you are extremely vulnerable to any infection and have to stay on the ward.

As Christmas time fell upon us, one of my best friends on the ward became seriously ill. He could barely move or speak for days and because he is such a character normally it was extremely upsetting to see, especially at that time of year.

On the ward you can develop strong bonds with your fellow patients. Often you have to alert the nurses with your emergency buzzer if for whatever reason they are unable to press it. You learn to keep an eye out for each other.

I contracted a mild infection a few days later but it was far less severe than his. As soon as you get a temperature the doctors begin treatment with antibiotics and thankfully these were sufficient to cure me. But I learnt it can be much worse. Some patients would have to have a catheter inserted and be taken 'upstairs' to the high dependency unit.

What was also scary was realising just how quickly people could go from being seemingly healthy and in just a few hours be completely knocked out.

Christmas was a sad time for me only made brighter by my family, friends and the nurses. I remember waking up on Christmas Day and two of the night staff had decorated special pillow cases and put our names on too. Inside were chocolates and a Satsuma- it was a fantastic gesture that really cheered me up!

As someone who loves Christmas and everything it stands for I found it a particularly difficult time in my treatment. I watched midnight mass from Liverpool Cathedral on my little television and admit I had a small lump in my throat.

In the nights that followed I often felt myself sinking into sadness. Night times were always the worst because I don't drop to sleep easily, leaving too much time to think.

If I'm being totally honest, I don't think death is something to be scared of, I see it very much as a natural part of life. Leukaemia is a strange condition because although there is much to be hopeful of, dying is always a possibility and although I'm not fearful of that, I do find the disease carries a lot of potential sadness that I am unable to shake off. Thinking about how devastated my family and girlfriend would be is very difficult.

For many nights, and still to this day, one image I can't get out of my head is watching a film of my own funeral. The sequence is always the same. The camera follows the coffin as it is brought into the church and then pans around to my parents who are inconsolable and both crying loudly.

COMMENTS (12)

Imagining your own funeral is a sign that you have accepted that death is a possibility and that, in your own way, you are prepared to deal with it. What you can't do is dwell on it. We can't dictate what life holds for us, but what we can control is the way we deal with what has been handed to us. *Pinkers*

I also envisioned your funeral in the early days of this adventure. However, in my fantasy, I appeared as a tragic yet serene heroine, facing the ordeal with grace, elegance and quiet dignity. Not wailing noisily with snot-slimed cuffs! As it is not going to be possible to reconcile our respective images, you will jolly well have to get better. Lots of love. *Mum*

What I have learned from you, is that you can't change what has happened, you just have to learn how to adapt and live with the way life is now and appreciate the simple things. *Katie*

Just wanted to wish you the very best of luck with your treatment. Your blog is great - well done. You will be welcome back at the Denby Dale Parish Council meetings anytime! *Terry and family*

A BLOG FOR FOOD LOVERS

April 24, 2007

Because your blood counts take so long to recover, when they are finally restored leaving hospital is as exciting as busting out of jail - I imagine.

It seemed to take an age but at last I could be released for a couple of weeks to allow my marrow to regenerate further and for me to recover psychologically. Living on a ward and not being allowed to leave can drive you insane.

But the best bit is still to come and anyone who is on a diet should look away now.

I was given specific doctor's orders to eat as much unhealthy food as I could possibly manage. The point being to replace weight loss during the chemotherapy and to bulk up ahead of the second lot.

Not only that, but salad was expressly forbidden!

It was like a dream come true.

When finally discharged I had the most amazing shop at a supermarket in my life. Everything that was normally off-limits was now fair game. Into the trolley went jam doughnuts, Danish pastries, huge multi-packs of crisps, cheesecakes and plenty of meat.

I would eat a fried breakfast nearly every morning. The scale of some of them was immense; verging on the obscene.

One morning I polished off three sausages, three pieces of bacon, three slices of black pudding, a tin of baked beans and toast.

I'm not going to lie to you, it was amazing, and well worth every drop of the ensuing meat sweats.

Some people find that after chemotherapy they are tired and it can take many months to recover fully.

For me I felt fine and, determined to put some bulk back on, I began a regime of light exercise.

I was soon able to run a reasonable distance, very slowly, but it felt great being active again. Each morning I would do a routine of push ups and sit ups and it drove me to get focussed on what lay ahead.

My time out was spent with friends and family and just resting at home. Everyone was brilliant to me and everywhere I went I would be fed up on roast dinners and unhealthy puddings.

You forget just how many little things you take for granted, like sleeping in your own bed or making a cup of tea for yourself whenever you like.

I even recall having an unusual sense of enjoyment while doing my first load of washing up - this buzz quickly faded.

Going back in was something I was not looking forward to but the break was crucial. It allows you to recharge your batteries and prepare yourself for the next step.

Oh, and I managed to put on nearly 5kg!

COMMENTS (7)

You seem to forget Ade, that everyone else put on 5kg too!!! It was worth it. *Cazza*

Sounds good that, full English every morning, all the choccies you can eat. *Liam*

You should get back on the University diet! Mei Sum's sausage dinner and a burger from Zain's with extra hot chilli sauce! Should probably stay off the Kirov/Kilroy vodka though!
Tom

Enjoying your blog, keep them up! *Debbie, Huddersfield*

PNEUMONIA
April 26, 2007

After my first bit of chemotherapy I developed a minor infection. Now I was about to experience just how ill someone with a very limited immune system can get.

Thankfully my second lot of chemotherapy went really well. The nurses gave me the same combination of anti-sickness and anti-inflammatory drugs that worked for me on the last day of my previous treatment. I wasn't sick once and was able to function as a normal human being throughout.

Then when my counts came crashing down I remained fine for well over a week. Things were going so well that boredom became the biggest battle. I would watch DVDs kindly donated by friends, and television in the day ward, but there are a lot of hours to kill in a day.

For most people, including myself, reading would be one of the few joys of having so much free time. Another cruel side-effect of the chemotherapy is that it can affect concentration. I found this made reading a really unpleasant experience.

I was so bored that I was almost excited when I got my first temperature. It was only very mild to begin with and, to be honest, the first two days were pretty good, I felt fine but just needed to sleep more.

However, things rapidly deteriorated. I was having horrific night sweats which were so bad my bed needed changing three times on some occasions. My fevers raged for hours with my body temperature just short of 40°C (104°F) - if it's any help the nurses' charts only run up to 40°C.

During these times I can remember attempting to speak and just burbling gibberish. I had to wear a Darth Vadar-like mask to help get the required level of oxygen into my system and calm a violent cough.

I can hardly remember the five days that passed after that night. People came to take my blood and check up on me but they were just brief blurs, lost in hours of perpetual fevers and sleep.

Throughout this difficult period the doctors and nurses were wonderful to me. I remember waking up some times and one of the nurses would be stroking my arm or just really keen to see how I was feeling. It was incredibly uplifting being supported in this way.

Antibiotics were tried but generated little response. The doctors then switched to anti-fungal medication which slowly began to make a difference. I can remember one of the doctors explaining how strong these tablets are.

He said: "In a minority of patients this drug can cause temporary blindness.

"If this does happen, don't panic, it's completely transient and will only last for a couple of minutes."

Thankfully my eyesight remained throughout.

We never really got to the bottom of what actually caused my pneumonia. It was explained to me that the lungs are dirty places and all of us breathe in fungal spores that surround us in the air. A normal immune system should be able to fight it off.

Then I went home again to recover further, devour shameful amounts of food, and prepare for my third cycle. Unfortunately, things didn't quite work out as expected.

COMMENTS (12)

Know we've only met briefly, but just wanted to say I think you're doing a cracking job with these blogs. *Sam C*

Good to hear you are at least getting tons of food and I'm glad that your spirits are still high. Keep up the blog mate, following it avidly here. Wishing you all the best. *Finlay*

You are truly an inspiration! I heard about you on Calendar and have just read your blog. I shall continue to keep up with your progress and want to wish you and your family and girlfriend Poppy all my best wishes. Stay strong. My prayers are with you all. *Susie*

TRANSPLANT
May 2, 2007

"You do realise there could be up to a 30% chance of dying during the transplant process. This means for every 100 patients treated in this way, up to 30 could die."

Initially my brain screamed at the consultant that I was fully aware of the percentage concept. Then, as I suppose the doctor intended, that figure transformed into real people, who really could die, in real life.

I always hoped I would be able to avoid a bone marrow transplant, or stem cell transplant as they are now called, and just carry on with the cycles of chemotherapy. But this wasn't to be.

Following my second cycle of chemotherapy my bone marrow, under the microscope, looked great. Good enough for the Acute Myeloid Leukaemia (AML) to be classed as being in remission.

Genetically, however, things were not quite so hunky-dory. Again my bone marrow had been sent away for further tests and the results were not good.

The abnormal cells associated with my secondary, chronic form of leukaemia, had increased from 20% to 50%, between the two sets of chemotherapy. Not only that, but they were becoming increasingly bizarre at a genetic level.

At this stage the crucial factor is whether a donor is available. Thankfully I have a common tissue type and a donor was identified quite quickly. This was vital because the results suggested that the chronic form was aggressive and the fear was it could trigger another outbreak of AML.

The Anthony Nolan Trust searched the European databases and found a match for me.

At the moment, if you are white and have a common tissue type, you are quite likely to find a match.

However, it can be much harder for ethnic minorities. My plea in this blog is that all readers, if they are not already, should consider becoming a donor. Please have a look at the Anthony Nolan site via the link.

Many more Asian, black, and mixed-race donors need to be found in order to prevent more lives being lost to leukaemia and other cancers of the blood.

There is also a lack of males on the register too.

The next post will contain more information about what it's like to donate stem cells.

So, the transplant itself.

Firstly the good news is it can be a lasting cure for leukaemia. The odds of being cured are also better than chemotherapy alone.

It also represents great hope. I don't know how much longer I would have lasted without it, but it probably wouldn't have been for much more than a year.

If you could just pop the new stem cells in with no side effects it would be fantastic. But, as you probably can imagine, it's not as simple as that.

For your body to accept the foreign cells you need to be exposed to even higher levels of chemotherapy and intense radiotherapy. This clears your bone marrow in preparation for the new stem cells to bed in.

Exposure to these greatly increases your chances of getting further cancers later in life.

There can also be problems if a conflict develops between the 'host's' body and the donor's cells. This is known as graft versus host disease, if this is severe it can also lead to death.

However, the best chance of being cured is if conflict develops between the new cells and the leukaemia. This is known as graft versus leukaemia and is highly desirable.

Throughout the process your immune system is entirely wiped out until the new stem cells begin rebuilding it. Because of this there is a huge infection risk.

In summary, the downsides are:

- Up to a 30% chance of dying.
- A lowered life expectancy because you are far more likely to develop secondary cancers.
- Infertility.
- You need your vaccinations again because it's like growing an immune system from scratch.
- If it goes well, you will have to be in isolation for four to five weeks.
- This is all on top of the usual vomiting and hair loss.
- I should also add my blood group will change from O+ to A+ - that of the donor's - after about six weeks.

Before I spoke to the doctors about the transplant, I always thought I would have to undergo some sort of operation. This is not correct.

The donor's cells are given just like a blood transfusion. Once in the blood stream the new cells just know where to go, which I have to say, is pretty bloody amazing.

Before my transplant began I had the strangest mixture of emotions; hope, enormous gratitude, apprehension, resentment that I had to go through it yet feeling incredibly lucky that there was a donor.

When a doctor reads out the following list of possible side effects in a dead pan voice, "nausea, severe infection, death," you know you're up against something serious. But I also know there are thousands of patients who have not only survived the procedure, but gone on to live full and healthy lives.

That was always a great source of strength for me.

COMMENTS (3)

I always thought you were common! *Tom*

Good to have you back. I am amazed at how much knowledge you have packed in in such a short time. Don't get despondent you are young and can do this. *Trish*

BONE MARROW DONATION - IT SHOULD BE CALLED STEM CELL DONATION REALLY
May 3, 2007

What would you say if I said stem cell donation differed little from giving blood?

You'd probably say something like, "Shut up Sudders, I'm tired of your online cancer whinging, and if I was a bone marrow donor someone would need to smash my spine."

I have a degree in Physiology, have spent five months in and out of a haematology ward, and I'm still staggered that I have only learnt what stem cell donation is really like.

There is a huge amount of confusion on the issue. I used to give blood but never thought about donating stem cells because I thought there was a slight risk of paralysis.

The reality is very different. In the UK, around 70% of all transplants are carried out using stem cells found in the regular blood stream.

If you wanted to get on one of the donor registers all you have to do is ask about it next time you give blood. Alternatively, you could get in touch with the Anthony Nolan Trust.

Specialists can tell from your blood whether you are a potential tissue match for someone or not. Your details are then entered onto one of the databases.

If you were a match for someone who needed a transplant, and you still wanted to help, you would be given a number of injections of a naturally occurring hormone called Granulocyte Colony Stimulating Factor (GCSF), four days prior to the donation.

This stimulates your bone marrow to increase blood cell production. For example, when you are ill, GCSF stimulates the marrow to make more white blood cells to fight off infection.

The injections are safe and the only side effect I experienced when I was given some on the ward was a slight ache in my bones.

A donor is then brought into hospital and hooked up to a machine called a cell separator. A needle is put in one arm and the blood goes into the machine. The stem cells are separated by centrifugation and flow into a bag. The other parts of the blood are then returned back to the donor through a different needle.

The whole process takes around four hours.

Current research shows that these types of stem cells are the best for curing leukaemia.

However, for some conditions such as aplastic anaemia, stem cells from the bone marrow are more desirable.

To get these cells a bone marrow harvest is performed. This can require a two-night stay in hospital. When I have a bone marrow sample I have to lie on my side in the foetal position. I am given a local anaesthetic and a needle is inserted into the bony bits at the back of my pelvis.

A donor is given a general anaesthetic and the same procedure is carried out but at multiple sites.

There is no bone-breaking or spine jeopardising - that is not to say it wouldn't be a bit sore in the morning!

None of these procedures are anything to be taken lightly and do represent a big commitment. All I ask is that readers have a look at the relevant websites and consider it next time they give blood.

I've been lucky - but many patients are still unable to find donors. Please visit the links below to find out more

www.anthonynolan.org.uk
www.blood.co.uk
www.ebmt.org

COMMENTS (8)

Great that you are trying to recruit more bone marrow donors, my husband registered when I was diagnosed. I never had a transplant as my brother was not a match, I just carried on with the chemo which, touch wood, has done the trick. Your blog brings back lots of memories to me (not pleasant ones though) and I can relate to it all. Keep your chin up and stay positive. *Judith*

Thought you'd like to know that one more person will be added to the registry very soon. I just filled in the forms today. I'd been meaning to do it for ages, you finally got to me! *Diana*

Grandma phoned me last week with an update and I'm now regularly reading 'the BLOG'. You're just amazing. Just to let you know we'll all be rooting for you here when you get 'under transplant conditions'. *Hilary, Rod & James*

Hoping that all goes well with the transplant. Your Blog makes compelling reading. Thank you for explaining the process so clearly. I am sure that the break and gourmet food has set you up. This bone marrow will be so grateful to join a healthy body that it will be pleased to work overtime for you. *Jamie*

There is no happiness like that of being loved by your friends and family. *Rebecca*

My husband had very similar experiences to yours. We think that your blog is fantastic and raises awareness of these types of illnesses. We were totally unaware of the whole situation and ignorant of the procedures and treatments. We sincerely hope that your raising of the whole issue will bring forth the response that you are striving for and whole-heartedly agree with your sentiments regarding the happiness that being loved by your friends and family is the most precious of gifts. We are rooting for you. *Madeline*

No Going Back
May 8, 2007

I wish none of this was happening to me, but it is.

How do I talk seriously to my girlfriend about dying much younger than I should?

Readers of previous posts will know how important having children is to me, so do we go for IVF knowing full well that by the time they are ten I could be dead?

What sort of impact would it have on their lives?

What does Poppy do then? Getting any life insurance will be virtually impossible so do I bother?

What about buying a house - will Poppy be able to downsize if I die earlier than expected?

Should I ditch saving for a pension?

What about holidays?

We both love to travel but I won't be able to go abroad for at least another year or so.

I wish we didn't have to address these questions, but we do.

This cruel and indiscriminate disease impacts not only on my life but also on others - especially Poppy's - and the depth of how much I hate and resent that fact is difficult to express.

Being told you will die much younger than you normally would is hard to come to terms with. "Anyone could get hit by a bus tomorrow, you don't know what's around the corner." That's what everyone keeps saying, but for me the 'could', in this metaphorical incident, has been replaced with a 'will - at some point'.

Also, why does everyone seem to think there are so many bad bus drivers out there?

I wish I didn't, but sometimes I think the best outcome would be if I died in the next couple of weeks.

Sorry.

I did say that when I started this blog it wouldn't be all doom and gloom but everyone has down days.

I'm lucky because I can snap out of mine pretty quickly - I've got a donor, a fantastic medical team on my ward, support of a wonderful girlfriend, family, friends and work colleagues.

Since being released from hospital in early March I have had some great times with all of them. Everyone has helped me feel better, just by keeping in touch, making me laugh or by buying me a pint.

People said to me when I told them that I was writing these blogs that it might help others who are in a similar situation. I don't know if that's the case, but from my point of view I have found writing them incredibly cathartic. All the comments have been lovely and I would like to thank everyone who has posted one.

Regarding the bone marrow transplant itself, obviously I'm nervous, but also highly confident that it will go well.

However, I have to say I'm sick of being asked when my "operation" is or "when my hip is being broken". It has become pretty obvious that there is a lot of confusion about what the transplant actually is.

I can't do much in my present condition but the one thing I can do is help raise awareness and clear up many of the myths surrounding bone marrow, or stem cell, transplants.

That's why I wanted to take part in a series of films, explaining the procedure, for www.examiner.co.uk.

My colleagues Gemma Castle and David Himelfield will be making a number of short video blogs explaining how my body is prepared for the transplant, the transplant itself, then attempt to capture what it's like to be in isolation.

From my point of view I hope that last stage is boring and uneventful. It can be a bit of a lottery with symptoms ranging from a slight skin rash to good old-fashioned death. For example, patients can experience severe pain due to the lining of their throat and gut being destroyed during the treatment.

Obviously I'm not too excited about that prospect but I suppose we will have to wait and literally see what happens.

COMMENTS (25)

I am absolutely glued to this blog. It's mind blowing. I sat some of the junior doctors down in the library at Preston Hospital the other day to read the blog. They commented that they learned more about your condition and the impact that it has upon your closest friends and family than reading a tonne of books. They have asked me to pass on my very best wishes. *Dr Thomas*

Short films? Interviews with Press Gazette? What's next - GMTV? I'm loving your work Adrian! Your blogs are great - witty, informative and this one made me cry. Proof you're in the right job! *Lucy*

I read the blog cover to cover (if you can do that on the net!). There's so much I didn't, and still don't, really understand about this shocking reality, thanks to you I'm one step closer. There aren't many people who would find the courage to express themselves so profoundly in a situation of this gravity so give yourself a huge pat on the back. *Christo p.s. Where did you get that hat?*

Just to let you know Adrian that your blogs are fantastic. Always brings a lump into my throat when I read them. Would like to take this opportunity to wish you good luck for next week and hope to see you again very soon. We are all thinking of you. *Super H*

You'll have your own cable channel before long. *Richard, Ellen and the bump*

You mention having children is important to you and that you are considering IVF. I don't know whether you are aware, but a fertility clinic could freeze your sperm at this stage, rather than you and Poppy having IVF now (or freezing embryos now). Then you would have the choice to use your sperm for IVF in the future, possibly for multiple attempts, rather than just one IVF cycle for creating embryos now before you become infertile. Sorry if you already knew that but I thought it was worth mentioning. Good luck with everything. *Anonymous*

Just watched the vids, good stuff - though some of the camera-work was appalling :) Best of luck for the transplant tomorrow. *Barry*

THANK YOU

May 9, 2007 3:42 PM

Throughout my illness I have been given the most tremendous support.

Firstly I would like to thank all the nurses, doctors and support staff on ward P3. They have been brilliant to me. Every time I have felt down someone has come in and cheered me up just by spending time with me or listening to me talk drivel.

I could not have come this far without them and I don't think I will ever be able to express my full gratitude to the team.

I also want to say thank you to my anonymous donor who has so generously given me a chance to live.

When I was diagnosed with leukaemia back in November it was like a huge rock being thrown into a pool, the ripples of which swept out across so many friends, family members and colleagues.

Their response has also been incredible raising a large sum of money for charities associated with leukaemia.

My friend Phil Driver ran the London Marathon for the Anthony Nolan Trust, in a pretty impressive four hours. He has also organised a big football tournament in Liverpool at which there will be a drive for new stem cell donors.

I hope he knows how grateful I am for all the effort and time he has personally put in.

Phil has now raised over £5,000 for the Anthony Nolan Trust.

My girlfriend Poppy invited members of her family and other friends to throw themselves down a six-mile white water rafting course in Scotland. This feat was made all the more impressive that one of the rafters was unable to swim.

They raised a further £4,200 for the Anthony Nolan Trust.

My mum, Kay Sudbury, works for a law firm in Nottingham called Browne Jacobson. The firm held a raffle and auction - where partners volunteered to work as slaves for the day - raising over £4,000 for Leukaemia Research.

Special mention has to go to Examiner photographer Andy Catchpool. He donated the £175 given to him for 25 years' company service to ward P3 where I am being treated. The ward is about to launch a huge improvement programme and his money will be put towards directly enhancing the facilities available for patients undergoing leukaemia treatment.

Thank you to all my family and friends who have helped me during this difficult time.

I'd also like to thank all my colleagues at work - thanks for everything you have done and for being so brilliant during a pretty terrible time in my life.

I have been really touched by the amazing levels of generosity and kindness shown towards me. You have no idea how much it has helped.

COMMENTS (8)

My mum told me a member of the Examiner staff had been diagnosed with cancer and because I had been there on work experience there last year I immediately went to check it out. Of all the people in the office, yours was the face and name I would have recognised best because I spent the day with you in the newsroom so I was shocked to see it was you. I have read your blog and think you're amazing. You seem to be fighting through with unbelievable bravery despite how hard it obviously is for you at the moment. By chance I happen to be taking part in the Race For Life this summer so I am doing my bit for Cancer Research. *Claire*

I'm one of the Biomedical Scientists that does your full blood counts down here on H floor! I've been watching your video diary and reading your blog and I think you are a truly amazing, inspirational person. It's fantastic to see things from a patients' point of view, as working in the lab we only see the analyzers and the numbers! So thanks for keeping us in touch with your progress and keep up that positive attitude. *Mel*

Good to hear you're out of hospital. I know from my own experience what a long and frustrating time it can be gradually building up your strength again. Just take your time, and when people ask how you are, the answer is always the same: "A little bit better than yesterday, but not quite as good as tomorrow!" *Andrew*

Good site! I'll stay reading! Keep improving! *Nika*

All the best for the transplant. I think that the way you are coping is a real inspiration to anyone reading your blog. I'm just so glad that you have a wonderful girlfriend in Poppy, and also family and friends to help you through. *Ruth x*

VIDEO BLOGS
May 16 - June 24, 2007
Between May 16 and June 24 Adrian posted 9 video blogs covering his treatment and isolation.

He was very much at his lowest ebb during this period, hating the isolation, tiredness and infections and wondering what the future would hold.

Watch them at www.baldyblog.freshblogs.co.uk

THE WAITING ROOM
September 3, 2007
Apologies for not updating this blog sooner.

I felt for a while that I should have written something but I was never quite sure what to say. The amazing comments that have come from the hundreds of people regularly taking an interest in my story have been unexpected and inspirational for me.

It's also been helpful knowing that the posts have provided a useful insight to people who will have to undergo a bone marrow transplant in the future.

I suppose it's with this group of people in mind that I've been most reluctant to write anything else. Much of my time post-transplant hasn't been much fun and I'm still nowhere near full-fitness.

I finally decided to write this post after talking to my grandma in Nottingham. Basically she's bullied me into writing it arguing that people respect honesty and the truth - even though it doesn't always make for pleasant reading. I think she's right, so here we go.

The first thing to say is I am waiting for the results of my final bone marrow sample. It's been sent away for analysis and the results will show that the leukaemia is either still here or gone completely.

I suppose the best of all outcomes would be the all-clear - of course it would. But people are already saying to me the champagne corks will be popping as if that's it - it's all over, life can resume as normal. But of course it can't; it will never be the same for me. I can never have children naturally, I will be dead probably by the time I'm 50.

No one seems to understand that it can never just stop there. There will be tests, getting ill, I still feel sick most days now, and there will always be that nagging worry over whether the disease will come back.

I am struggling to accept the cost at which this treatment has come and often flash-forward to my attempts to sound positive when friends and family call regarding the 'good-news'.

And that's the best outcome.

The other alternative is the cancer, somehow, has managed to survive. A significant part of me has come to the conclusion that if those cells can withstand that level of radiotherapy and high-dose chemotherapy then maybe they have earned their right to flourish and to take me down with them.

Further treatment is something I am incredibly reluctant to have. I certainly don't want to have a bone marrow transplant again. In some ways I wish the doctors would just say: "Sorry, there's nothing more we can do," at least that would rid me of the constant anxiety, the restless nights, the long days on my own not feeling well enough to do anything but well enough to be bored.

At least a clear six months to live would mean I could plan for some incredible trips and parties. If you're going to pop your clogs you may as well do it in style!

On the outside I think I have kept good control over my emotions but on the inside I'm really struggling. I've never been a good sleeper so night times are always the worst.

Talking about God seems almost taboo in this country. No one outside of religious groups seems comfortable speaking openly about him - unless to blame him for all the ills of the world - but I feel it's important I share this experience.

My last week and a half in isolation was an awful period for me. I'd not eaten in that time, my stomach was constantly sore, I felt so alone and cold. During my entire illness I had never prayed to be made better - only to avoid the bone marrow transplant.

Inside that room, on those eight days or so, all I prayed for was to feel that there was something else that cared and loved for me; but nothing happened. I was unquestionably alone. I didn't expect a flash of lightning, or the appearance of some biblical apparition, I only hoped for a kind of intrinsic sense that there was more to all this than just me, lying there curled up, tears running gently from my eyes.

I have always tried to pray for other people and had a burgeoning faith. So, for me, this experience, when I was at my absolute lowest, will stay with me for however long I have left to live.

Yet interestingly it was a hospital chaplain who was one of the greatest helps to me through these difficult times. He would pop in at least once a week and chat with me about anything and everything. We would have a laugh together and I can't tell you how wonderful it was to converse with someone who wasn't medically or emotionally connected to me or make inquiries as to how many times I had "opened my bowels" that day.

You see the problem is being cooped up in that box for so long affects different people in different ways. For me, I found being 'attacked' psychologically, as well as having your insides reduced to pulp, very difficult to bear. Some of my treatment took place at 2am with observations around 6am. This meant on top of everything my sleep was always broken. I did joke with the nurses that they may as well have gone the whole hog and stuck me in an orange boiler suit while playing white noise through the radio.

I'm not an angry and bitter person but I hated how my 'treatment' was turning me into one. I was only allowed to have three visitors for the five weeks so obviously chose Poppy and my parents. I love my mum and dad - and hate snapping at them - but the situation just made me so irritable.

I still don't think I fear dying; it's anger and sadness that I feel most now. I torture myself with daily viewings of the Jeremy Kyle chat show where horrible ex-partners, whose sense of self-importance seems to have replaced their brains, scream at each other for twenty minutes about the custody of their neglected and un-loved children.

There are people throughout our society who are having children who simply should not have the right to. They are brought up in loveless and broken homes so it's little wonder that youngsters emerge from this moral vacuum to make the lives of their neighbours, teachers and everyone else a misery. It's also no surprise they join gangs and have no compunction about stabbing or shooting their peers.

I get angry that my natural right to have children has been ripped away from me.

Sometimes I want to punch one of the walls in my flat, but then I glance down at my scrawny arms, which bear more resemblance to pipe-cleaners, and think better of it.

The sadness I feel is for the time I have lost, and if this leukaemia can't be beaten, then for all the happy times that I know could have been.

The results are coming and I can't help feel that all this sitting at home, my mind being gently eroded by the banality of daytime television, is like being in the strangest, and cruellest, of waiting rooms.

COMMENTS (16)

Your story continues to move me and I hope you won't mind me passing on this blog entry to the school staff - as you know, your Dad was Head here before me and I know several of his ex-colleagues follow your story. My thoughts and prayers are with you and your family. I am sure your courage is a great comfort to others with leukaemia. Hang on in there! *Jenni*

I know from our conversations that you have been concerned about posting this. Your Grandma is right and I'm proud that you had the courage to continue your writing and post it. You needed to give a true account of your experience to inform everyone of the reality of the disease and not try to soften the blow. It's a cruel disease affecting all aspects of your health and life. You've told me that writing this blog has been a great focus of your energy and I hope that the honesty of such a beautiful and emotive piece of writing has helped you process your thoughts and emotions. We're all in the waiting room with you. *Love Jen*

Please do not be concerned about writing this. You are telling the truth and people who have got to have this treatment will thank you for that. We who have not had treatment will never know what you have had to go through and still continue to. The people who have had this will understand you completely and the people who have not will be well prepared for what to expect because of your selfless actions doing this blog! I can understand your anger a little, my daughter (15) has got to have IVF to preserve her fertility. When other girls are worrying about make up etc she is worrying about her future. Do not let it get you down. I admire you for what you have done Adrian and I am sure that a lot more people do as well. *Dawn*

VIDEO BLOG
September 5, 2007

September 5 saw his blog carry another video - this time concentrating on clearing up some of the myths attached to bone marrow donation. It was to be the start of his campaign to raise awareness.

Watch the video at www. baldyblog.freshblogs.co.uk

LINE OUT
September 10, 2007

The wait goes on. I've still not heard anything so continue to wait nervously.

I'm not sleeping brilliantly but apart from that I'm fine.

The good news is that my Hickman Line, that tube running out of my chest, has been removed from my body. It's literally been a part of me since December and has undoubtedly been a big part of my treatment.

Every time blood needed to be taken, or chemicals administered - which was most of the time - the Hickman line, named Fred by my aunt, has made it all possible without the use of needles.

Since emerging from isolation at the end of June I have had to go back into hospital twice with serious, but thankfully quite manageable infections. In both cases bacteria has somehow got into the line and caused me to become ill. It's scary how poorly you get in a very short space of time.

In both incidents I went from being well to being re-admitted within two hours. Powerful antibiotics quickly remedied the situation on both occasions.

It's strange not having it dangling out of my torso. You do get used to them quite quickly but I hope I don't need another one inserted in the future.

How do they get it out? Simple, they just pull it out! It sounds horrific and now being the veteran of countless 'undesirable' hospital procedures I have to admit feared the worst.

But for anyone who is wondering what it is like I can report it's refreshingly painless. All the doctor did was inject some anaesthetic where it emerges from the skin, wrap it around his fingers and pull.

Some patients take their line home as a memento - I was not that bothered.

COMMENTS (8)

Fantastic I'm really happy to hear how well you've done. Stay healthy. *Laura*

I can't even begin to imagine what you are going through but I thank you for sharing it with me and thousands of others I wish you the best of luck you are doing a fantastic job by trying to help others you're an inspiration not many people would be able to find the courage or strength to do this, all the best for the future. *Kelly*

I just saw your story on TV, and I think it's amazing what you are doing. Your story has really touched me. I will keep you in my prayers. Thank you for what you are doing :). *Aneta*

GREAT NEWS
September 11, 2007

Finally some great news - I've been given the all clear.

It's hard to describe how relieved and elated I feel. I found out earlier today when I phoned the hospital braced for bad or no news.

I was told simply that the results had come back and there was no sign of either type of the disease.

After living for ten months with a complicated form of leukaemia I had feared the worst. When the doctor told me there was no sign of the disease in my last bone marrow sample I asked him to check, and then double check the results, before I could finally take them in.

I put the phone down and immediately phoned Poppy, followed by my parents. It was refreshing to have some good news to tell them all at last.

After speaking to them I sat back in my arm chair and the weight of a hundred different emotions just seemed to be lifted from me. For the first time in months, death, sadness and worry were no longer there. Temporarily it was bliss and I just felt so thankful and grateful to be alive. I could feel a lump in my throat, put my head in my hands and cried a few tears of happiness. I remember wiping my eyes then returning to the task of texting and phoning my friends.

For the next two hours my phone was in meltdown with messages and calls from friends, family and colleagues. It was such a good feeling to be able to share the good news with people who have supported me so well since the end of last November.

I know I have written about the downsides of my treatment but today was about being given a second chance of life through the kindness and generosity of a complete stranger.

I'm so pleased that for the time being there will be no more gruelling treatment, no more unpleasant procedures, no more lengthy stays in hospital.

So what do you do when you've been given news like that? Well if my life had been a film I'm sure I should have done something spectacular involving champagne and a huge party. Maybe there would be a power ballad playing in the background.

But real life is very different to that. I had the weekly food shop to do so found myself in the local Asda. I might have survived a bone marrow transplant but failure to complete this task might have resulted in Poppy killing me! (Just a little joke love).

I hope now the countdown to returning to my normal life and work can begin. In the next five or six weeks I intend to begin light exercise and try to restore some strength to my body.

This post has been speedily written but I will be finishing off this blog with a few more entries in the coming weeks. I'm not 100% yet but I am determined to get myself as strong and as fit as I can.

I'm trying so hard not to finish with a cliche but inevitably I have failed. All I can say is I am simply over the moon.

COMMENTS (31)

Brilliant news about the Hickman Line removal but even more brilliant is the news that the Bone Marrow transplant has been successful. Get out the Champagne and really enjoy your weekend and the fact that you have got your life back! Love to Poppy and your family. *Jamie*

Oh Adrian what wonderful, weightlifting news this is, even my eyes leaked a bit on hearing it! *Annie*

Saw the tea time news - fantastic! I cried tears of joy for you, I am so delighted for you with the news - you have been a true inspiration to all. *Pam*

Really pleased for you, you've been through so much. Hopefully you can get back to living your life soon. *Pat*

Congratulations… that was wonderful to read! Thank you so much for sharing your journey with all of us, and all of the best luck in the future to you. *Jen*

ANDY SAGE

October 2, 2007

Andy Sage was one of the funniest and most courageous men I've ever had the privilege to know.

The 42-year-old Sheffield brickie was my best friend on ward P3 throughout the 10 months of my treatment.

He was one of those human beings who would light up a room and could get even the most miserable sods in there laughing. He was a massive character in every sense of the word measuring well-over six foot and weighing in, I'm sure he wouldn't mind me saying, at just a little over rotund.

Such was the size, strength and heart of the man he always, for me, carried an aura of invincibility.

When you're in a terrible situation, like anyone undergoing intensive treatment for cancer, you need people to help keep your spirits up and Andy did that in spades. His banter was incredible and wit as quick as any stand-up comedian.

It was obvious how much the staff on the ward liked him too - despite him always trying to wind them up and spend as little time on the ward as possible.

"If you were proper nurses, like them in Casualty," he'd say, "We'd be fit and out of here in two weeks."

His positive attitude was incredible too. If you recall from my earlier posts after chemotherapy for leukaemia you have to spend weeks on the ward until your immune system recovers. During that time he would grab his drip stand and encourage me to join him in doing laps of the ward.

I will always hold onto this strange image of this huge bloke with his red cap, and Sheffield United top on, flying past the nurses' station before settling down for the afternoon war movie.

To say Andy was a big United, or Blades fan, was an understatement. He was always giving fans of the city's other football team, Sheffield Wednesday - or Wednesdayites - lots of grief. It was hilarious watching these fans, patients and staff, engaging in this good natured sparring.

You have to spend so many hours in that place so to be with someone who can generate that level of energy and laughter was incredibly helpful to me and everyone else involved there.

One of my favourite memories of Andy was his love of the football computer game Championship Manager. The general idea of this game is you take charge of a team and guide them to success and trophies - but Andy had other ideas.

I remember one day he had this huge smile beaming out from behind his laptop. I asked him what he was up to, assuming he had steered the Blades to Champions League glory. Far from it. He explained he had taken over Sheffield Wednesday and was revelling in getting them relegated and financially ruined. He'd do things like buy 11 left-backs for sums vastly in excess of their asking price. When players got upset at the situation he would just ignore them and carry on regardless.

Andy had a harder time in hospital than me. He had a number of very serious infections and had to be taken upstairs to the High Dependency Unit on a couple of occasions.

He has already featured in my blog (Christmas and getting ill) because he was so poorly over the festive period. It was awful seeing him so poorly on Christmas Eve and Christmas Day. When characters like that can hardly move or talk it's horrible to witness.

But he never let any of it get him down. He kept fighting all the time and that was inspirational to me. After a week he was back on his feet and mocking me for vomiting so loudly!

Our treatment seemed to be linked. We both had two cycles of chemotherapy at the same time, both of which failed. We then started our bone marrow transplants about a week apart. It never crossed my mind that he wouldn't get over the disease.

As you have probably gathered by now Andy didn't make it. On the same week I got my good news I learnt Andy had not been so fortunate. I think his leukaemia had been much more aggressive than mine and the transplant had been unsuccessful. To sum up how devastated I am, and everyone who knew him was, is too difficult to put into words.

Although this last story might make for uncomfortable reading I wanted to include it because I know it would have made Andy laugh. After the transplant we were in semi-regular text message contact. I knew towards the end he was very ill and you know from personal experience you don't want to be bothered with lots of phone calls or messages.

On the Saturday while I was still waiting for my results I got a text from Andy saying his transplant had failed and that he'd been given four months to live. Then just hours after receiving my news on Tuesday I got the following text from Andy's phone:

"As usual I will have the last word. I would like you to join me on Saturday at Grenoside Crematorium to celebrate my life, love Andy."

Because Andy was such a big character my assumption was he had organised a big event with friends and family before he finally died.

I thought this was incredible and turned up to the event really looking forward to seeing him - I had even brought a card addressed to Andy. Then the hearse turned up with a large coffin in the back. To say I was shocked was an understatement.

The message must have been sent out under instructions from Andy by one of his relatives.

Although this story sounds a bit embarrassing I know it would have made Andy laugh. I can almost hear him saying: "So you came to my funeral thinking I would still be alive? You bloody idiot!" - Or words to that effect.

I should add that his funeral service was packed with hundreds of well-wishers, some in Blades and Wednesday tops, and the first song was the Jam's Going Underground - what a legend!

Andy was a terrific human being and the world seems a bit worse off for losing a character as big as he undoubtedly was. Despite my good news his family were so kind to me at the funeral and wake that followed.

His death makes me appreciate just how lucky I have been and even more determined to make the most of whatever time I have left. Like anyone who had the fortune to meet Andy, I will never forget him.

COMMENTS (14)

I didn't know Andy all that well, but he helped me more than he ever knew. When Adrian was first diagnosed I was very worried about him being by himself in the hospital with the weight of this illness hanging over him. Knowing Andy was there made it much easier - I knew that Ad would be kept entertained by this big man with his big personality and infectious humour. *Poppy*

I suffered more than enough from Andy Sages' wit on many occasions… as I am a Wednesday fan working on the ward he and Adrian were unfortunate enough to be on… It is hard to begin to explain how, as a member of staff you draw a line between what is work and what you try not to take home with you… patients such as Adrian and Andy through no fault of their own, make it so much harder, because they are people you cannot become in any way detached from. Sadly I had been on holiday for a fortnight and was in Spain when Andy sadly passed on. and funnily enough deemed myself unfortunate to miss his funeral, as funerals go. It was apparently the nearest thing to a laugh you are ever going to have but I would have expected nothing less from a bloke who's only fault was the football shirt he wore, day in, day out on the ward. *Andy P3*

I didn't know Andy, but I know he really kept Ade going when he was in hospital, and Ade thought a lot about him. It's so sad that the outcome for Andy wasn't the same as for Ade. I'm sure he will be deeply missed. *Nellie*

I never met Andy - that is my loss. Everything Ad tells me about him indicates what a grand chap he was - coping with the worst that could be thrown at him with style and humour: taking a younger man under his wing as well. *Adrian's Grandma*

My parents used to run The Hallamshire Hotel, Andy's local! Andy was like an uncle to me in my early years, and everyone there misses him including Ann and Paul. Thank you for writing such a beautiful piece on Mr Fruitcake. *Lily*

REPLIES TO READERS
October 2, 2007

Hello everyone. There's been good news as you know, and unfortunately bad news too. It's been a difficult couple of weeks as you will have gathered from my previous post. I was also yesterday diagnosed with a case of chronic graft versus host disease so have been feeling less than 100% for a little while - just as it looked like I was getting back on my feet. Well, at least it gives me something else to bore you with at a future date!

I really wanted to take this opportunity to reply to some of the fabulous comments I have received regarding being given the all clear. I don't get chance to go online everyday but again the level of support has been incredible so here we go.

Mohammed - thanks for getting in touch and for your kind words. I'm really sorry to hear about your niece. Her treatment will be hard but I have found the love and support and family and friends is invaluable. It will be difficult but lots of people, all around the world, do make full recoveries every day from this dreadful disease. Every different type of leukaemia is different, as is its treatment. If I can help you, your niece and your family in anyway, please drop me another comment and I will email you back. Best wishes.

Hi Liz - Love your comments. It's really good just to be able to think about normal things, like footie, and England playing well definitely gave me a boost. I was in isolation when Forest got dumped out of the play-offs by Yeovil. I was at one of my lowest points so thanks a lot for that lads!

Annie - Thanks again for your support. I hope you liked the comment I posted on your site. Sincere best wishes to you and Steven. Great stuff that Glivec!

Pat and all at Press Gazette - Cheers for the interest and following the story. I always joke with the lads at work that a negative outcome would have probably made for a better tale but you can't have everything!

Hi Julie G. Thanks for being such a good friend and delighted to hear your good news too.

Susan Leigh - It does feel good having that bloody line out and when your time comes I PROMISE it doesn't hurt! Really good luck with your transplant. There are so many success stories out there and it can be a fantastic cure for leukaemia. If you would ever like to get in touch feel free to post another comment and I can get hold of your email and reply to you personally. Best wishes.

Nicole Martin - Hi Nicole. Delighted that you have been given the all clear. It must have been incredibly difficult going through treatment like this with a young child as well. Many thanks for getting in touch. Where in Sheffield do you live?

Hi Jacquie - Really sorry to hear about your son's close friend losing his fight against cancer. It's is such a difficult time and I know from experience that words don't really make it any easier so I won't ramble on. On a lighter note I was in Leeds last week and virtually bumped into Katherine Tate as she attended the premiere of her latest film at the Vue cinema. Small world eh? I resisted the urge to go up to her and irritate her with any of her catchphrases.

Alison - Thanks for your kind words Alison. I know how much they have helped me and my family.

Samantha - Thanks so much for getting in touch.

Andy, Anne, Tom and Harry - Thank you for all your comments and supporting my family in the way you have. Auntie Mary has also written to me and I will get back to her in the coming days. It's great to hear from you all and I hope life is treating you all well.

Thanks Jon - All the best to you too.

Laura Oakley - How goes it? Bloody lovely to hear from you. I hope you are pleased that your token northern friend is hopefully on the mend. My mates in Huddersfield always laugh at me when I tell them that in Essex (where we did our journalism course together) people thought I sounded really northern. You've not heard anything yet. As my good friend Jacko once remarked I'm like little Lord Fauntelroy up here. When I get back on my feet will be heading down to London - would be great if you and any other Harlow members could be there. Still in touch with Will, Ash (recently wed) and Lucy Twitchin.

Laura Garbas: Hi Laura - Your kind words are really appreciated. So sorry to hear about your cousin. Leukaemia truly is such a cruel and indiscriminate disease. Determined to make the best of the opportunity I have been given. Please pass on my regards to all those at the NCTJ - and if you know Lisa, Sara and Ken, please say hello.

Rob Irvine - Thanks Rob. I saw that you gave over one of your posts to promote my blog. Much appreciated and thanks so much for your interest.

Rob - Cheers dude. What are you up to these days?

Danny Holland and Craig Graney - Not seen you lads for a while but thanks so much for your support and interest. I hope everything in Pinxton/Normo is going ok. Maybe one day I will be fit enough to re-visit Ches or Le Mansfield for a night out. Ben says you are still playing 5-a-side too. Would be excellent one day to get fit again, have a kick around, then sup a lager shandy in the Miners. Take it easy and peace out.

Lynda Lawrence - I hope TV captured the real me; the cold, relentless hack that you at Residents Against Windturbines know only too well. It would be really good to get back to work and start reporting on some of these important local issues again. Best wishes to you, your family (I think I met your husband and daughter once) and all those campaigning for their local area.

Liz Boffey - I think your description of this disease as "awful" really sums it up. I'm sorry about your bad news, it must have been devastating to lose Will at just 22. It's only people like you who have any idea what a nightmare leukaemia is for the sufferer and those closest to them. For you to have supported me in this way, in such a positive and encouraging fashion, can only inspire me to make the most of the tremendous opportunity it looks like I have been given. All my thoughts and best wishes.

Hi Dawn - Thanks for all your comments over the last couple of months. Hope you like the comment I have recently posted on Rebecca's site. Sounds like things are looking up for her and your family. Thinking about you.

Natalie Willacy - Thank you so much for taking time to comment on my site. There has been so much support especially from people like yourself who know what fighting cancer is really like. You are so right, the support of friends and family is a huge help. I wish your mum all the best for her treatment but I imagine you are giving her some tremendous support, which is all you can do. I really hope your mum and family get some good news soon. ADx

Dear Jan and Paula - I could never forget you! You truly were the stars of the Total Body Irradiation video (number 4) and I've been told you did a wonderful job. That's one of the videos I still find too difficult to watch but everyone who's seen it said you were both excellent. When I get over this last hurdle I will come in and see you. Once again you both helped make one of the most difficult times in my life much more bearable so thanks once more. See you soon. Cheers Ben.

Local - Hi, sorry I don't know your name. My plans now are to get my strength back and start exercising again. That is why this latest news of the chronic graft versus host disease has been such a smack in the teeth. It sounds a bit pathetic but I'd just like to get back to normal life, including work!

Mark Leighton - Hello! Great to hear from you again. When I'm better would be great to see you again. Where are you living now and how is medicine treating you (no pun)? Anymore outings as the Incredible Hulk/robot dancing?

Brigitte Balestra - Merci Brigitte, vous êtes trés gentille!

COMMENTS (13)

Hi Adrian, thank you so much for your post on Becky's Caringbridge site. Hope that you will soon begin to feel better again and get back to work. You will never bore us with your stories as they are so honest and from the heart. All the best to you and your family. *Dawn*

Such an inspiring blog, your thoughts and comments have made me realise how lucky I am and I will never again moan about everyday things again! Well, maybe I might but I will certainly give myself a kick up the back side for doing so. *Ally*

A TOUCH OF CHRONIC GRAFT VERSUS HOST DISEASE
October 4, 2007

Just when everything seemed to be falling into place I have had another kick in the teeth. Yet again it's potentially very serious, possibly untreatable, but if it was anything less than that I am sure you would refuse to read on any further - and quite right too.

I have a suspected outbreak of chronic Graft versus Host Disease (cGvHD). It has attacked my skin leaving it flakier than a flapjack and as sore as salt and vinegar crisps on a mouth ulcer.

So sit back and let me tell you a tale of a red raw epidermis, high dose steroids and the undeniably homoerotic application of baby oil.

It all started about two weeks ago. I noticed my skin was not holding onto its moisture as it once did. To begin with it was nothing serious but, for the first time in my life, I found myself regularly applying moisturisers.

I still have bi-weekly check-ups at the hospital so I reported it to the doctor who has been looking after me.

He said to keep an eye on it but it was probably a side-effect from the Total Body Irradiation and would pass after a couple of months.

Clutching a big pot of E45 cream I returned home happy. Things then slowly began to deteriorate further.

What I did find interesting is the incredible amount of advice so many people seem to be able to dispense in this subject area. I was told about lots of different products, some of which I'd never heard of, and was thoroughly briefed on how to "exfoliate" successfully.

Then the baby oil came into play!

It was the only substance that would stop my skin drying out immediately and although a little inhibited about applying the greasy lubricant all over my naked body, let me tell you, it soon became a not all together unpleasant experience.

Would I go as far to say it made me feel macho? Yes I would.

This was satisfactory for a couple of days but then the problem became really unmanageable.

My skin was blossoming in shades of puce and its integrity was rapidly disintegrating. This meant some days my body was unable to regulate its temperature so even though my flat was roasting I felt unbelievably cold.

My eyes started to tighten making it very difficult to see out of until eventually all bits of my skin started to dry up.

Waking up in the mornings was unbearable. The backs of my legs and areas surrounding my shoulders were cracked and to move them was very painful. The only temporary relief I could get was to plunge into a bath filled with an emollient lotion. It was bliss.

Unfortunately, the effects of this bath would only last for about 15-minutes before the whole scaly process would begin in earnest once more.

I think the final straw came at the weekend when I asked Poppy (my girlfriend) to apply some oil to my back and around my shoulders.

Poppy speaks: "I asked Adrian to lift his arms up so I could moisturise his sides. As he did so, the underside of his arm was stretched from its normal, creased position. Normally, one would expect the skin to stretch out in response to this movement. Adrian's did not. Several large, bleeding cracks appeared in his already sore skin. I'm still cringing."

The next day it was back into hospital and urgent treatment began.

So what is Graft Versus Host Disease?

I think I mentioned it in an earlier post but it's probably important to re-cap here.

The graft refers to the donor cells that have engrafted and replaced my old bone marrow. I am the host. Ever since the transplant I have been on immunosuppressant drugs to stop conflict developing between my new cells and my body.

Bone marrow produces white blood cells which help protect your body against anything that shouldn't be there i.e. anything that it recognises as being foreign. This includes any remaining leukaemic cells which have somehow managed to survive the massive doses of chemotherapy and radiation bombardment.

The key GvHD symptoms you are told to watch out for include:

- Skin rash
- Sickness
- Diarrhoea

I developed a rash earlier on in my treatment which responded well to topical steroid creams. Because this happened before 100 days after the date of my transplant this is called acute GvHD.

Any flare-up after 100 days is referred to as being chronic. Because my skin was just drying up and getting redder alarm bells were not initially ringing in my head.

I was about a week away from coming off my immunosuppressants when this outbreak took place. Again dermatologists sliced out a small section of the skin on my arm to confirm whether it is indeed cGvHD and my doctors prescribed a very high dose of steroid tablets.

As my new immune system develops, and the drugs controlling this reaction are reduced, my white blood cells are starting to attack rapidly growing cells in my body. This means my skin is a bit of a target at the moment. But it's also dangerous because your new defences can start to attack your liver. Thankfully, tests show my liver is still functioning well at this stage.

My new treatment is two-fold.

- Increase the dose of the regular immunosuppressant drugs.
- The steroids come in and stop the new white blood cells, from my newly engrafted bone marrow, from working as 'well' as they are.

Thankfully I seem to be responding. The change in my skin, within 24 hours, has been incredible. No more problems have surfaced yet so I have to be optimistic that this situation can be contained. Some people are not so fortunate and the condition can run away from them, becoming incurable.

I am grateful to have seen such a change in such a short space of time, but as you know I was so close to getting back to normal life - and work. I'm annoyed and frustrated that this latest problem will delay matters further.

Sometimes it seems like it's never going to end.

COMMENTS (15)

Hi Ade, oh my God. I'm glad the baby oil had some use but I think that maybe we shouldn't set up our beauty tip column just yet! I hope that it's settling down and feeling more comfortable in the very near future and your bathing ritual in the mornings can shorten soon! *Em*

I'm sure the treatment will kick in and sort you out. The steroids will make you really happy!! Is it cyclosporin you're on? Just keep positive and I'm sure things will work out. *Liz*

Keep your spirits up Adrian - it will end sometime, you are too determined for it not to. I look forward to hearing that you are whipping this cGvHD. *Annie*

I'm sorry to hear of your latest set back and I only hope and pray that you return back to good health very soon. *Natalie*

I've just seen your blog for the first time, after Maggie, ward sister at Rotherham, told me about it yesterday. We spoke briefly when you came down to have a look round the unit. Glad your treatment is going well and always stay positive and keep smiling it helps. Congratulations on your award something good has come out of you being ill I suppose! *Carl*

BALDY'S BLOG SCOOPS NATIONAL AWARD
October 12, 2007

I'm delighted to be able to tell you that the blog has won a prestigious national award from the Guild of Health Writers.

Baldy's Blog won best online feature award at a glitzy-do at the Foreign Press Association, off the Mall, in London.

I know everyone says it but I genuinely didn't expect to win. I had, after-all, been in hospital that morning for a check-up and things are not going quite as smoothly as I had hoped regarding the latest complication - but more on that another time!

I was told a while ago that I had been short-listed so Poppy and I were determined to make the most of our trip to London. Not winning didn't really matter, it was just a great opportunity to escape from Sheffield, get dressed up and have a really good evening. And that is exactly what we did.

As I mentioned in the last post the steroid treatment has helped make me feel a million times better.

I can now eat a full meal, without feeling sick, and drink a bit more like I used to. The only downside, as you can see from the pictures, is that they are causing my face to swell-up much like that of an eastern European shot-putter or one of those blokes from the World's Strongest Man.

I look like I should be pulling trucks with my engorged neck and boggly eyes bulging out.

Earlier in the day, that was getting me down and the amount of chemicals in my body were leading to some strange emotions.

To try and calm these down we caught the train and treated ourselves to some good food and a bottle of wine.

We then met our friend Olie near our hotel for a few more drinks before heading over for a champagne reception at Carlton House Terrace. There were delicious canapés, followed by a bit more champagne, before we were treated to a speech from the writer and broadcaster Phil Hammond. You might recognise him from episodes of Have I Got News For You - his articles also feature regularly in Private Eye.

And then it was straight to the awards and I was up first. I couldn't believe it when they read my name out. I was totally overwhelmed. Thankfully, I didn't have to give a speech because I hadn't prepared anything.

I received a certificate and a cheque for £1,000. All I could hear was applause and Poppy letting out strange squeals of delight and excitement!

After the event lots of people involved with the Guild came up to me and said how good they thought the blog was and how it had helped de-bunk some of the myths surrounding leukaemia and bone marrow transplants.

I was really flattered and humbled.

All the way through these posts my family and friends have always said they like them - but, let's face it, they always were going to. You're not going to go up to someone with a potentially terminal illness and tell them, that on top of everything, their writing is awful. So to be recognised by such esteemed professionals was truly rewarding.

By the way the judging panel included, Dr Kamran Abbasi, Editor, Journal of the Royal Society of Medicine and Editor-in-chief of OnMedica; Jenny Hope, Medical Correspondent for the Daily Mail; Sara Jamison, Sales and Marketing Director, LighterLife (sponsors of the event); Jeremy Laurance, Health Editor at The Independent; Jane Symons, Editor of Sun Health and John Von Radowitz, PA News Science Correspondent.

After that, Pops and I hit the town. We found a nice little restaurant and, you know what, had a few more drinks.

I had an excellent night and it was so much fun after an otherwise bloody terrible year.

"Clean palm, dirty neck," as shot-putters say.

COMMENTS (21)

What wonderful news. Well done! You deserve it. Keep the chin up and keep smiling. Look forward to seeing you again very soon. *Super H!*

What can I say dude - it is absolutely tremendous to hear that you won that fantastic award !! You look so chuffed holding that certificate! *Mike*

Massive congratulations Adrian. You are such a worthy winner and I am not surprised one bit that your blog was picked out by the judging panel. It sounds like you had a fantastic night. You and Poppy both look very glam! Keep up the good work. I think the bookshelves are calling you now! Well done once again. *Julie*

Congratulations mate. I'm really pleased your hard work has had some reward and sounds like you had a very good night. You couldn't drink that much in uni so something's definitely working. Stay well and see you soon. *Andy*

Well done big guy (just a term of endearment not a reference to steroid abuse!) So pleased and proud of you buddy, properly deserved. A big bit of light at the end of what has been a rather dark tunnel. Hope you both had a wicked time, sounds quite boozy. I look forward to seeing you again next week belting out such classics as "Let's get ready to rumble" and "I am the one and only". The first of many awards I feel. What do you have to do to get on ITV's "Pride of Britain" though Ade? Scandalous! *Olie*

Congratulations on a well deserved award! (yes, I'm proud to admit that I'm totally biased)... Just read the latest hot-off-the-screen chapter... breaking news at 2.15am and flowing as readily as those celebratory drinks! A good read as always and some great pics! *Mike*

Congratulations Adrian. A well deserved award for an excellent blog. Your writing has helped so many people understand the in's and out's of leukaemia and have a little smile along the way. Well done mate. *Gavin D*

Well done! Adrian you thoroughly deserved to win. No speech though, you should have hogged the stage until they dragged you off! Hope you had a fantastic night. *Ben*

Mrs James would be proud of you!! Your face is lovely the way it is. *Cazza xxxx*

Nice one Ad. I'm so proud and may I say Pops is looking lovely on the photo. I hope you had a fantastic day mingling with the big wigs of the medical journalist world. A well deserved award. *Jen x*

What do you mean - course we'd tell you if you were writing a pile of p**! Nice one mate! *iMac*

I've been following your blog for over a month now, as I found it just before I went in to get my bone marrow transplant. I just wanted to say I really think that you deserve that award, as you have helped me, and so many others no doubt, go through such a tough time. I was a little hesitant as to what to expect before going in there, but you had everything written in straightforward terms that I could understand and you didn't gloss over the bad bits. It made me a lot calmer going in and I was discharged today, just four weeks after starting the prep chemo. *Kim*

FAT FACE ON TOUR '07
October 23, 2007

Last week when I realised I would need another three months of treatment it's fair to say it got me down a bit. The next phase is extremely complicated and not well-understood so I will explain further in the next post.

To boost my spirits I took a road trip to see more of the friends who have been so helpful to me throughout the last year. As I mentioned before, despite bloating my face and body, the steroids are actually making me feel pretty good, so I thought, 'Let's get away and do something positive'.

When I started writing this blog I didn't really want to include posts like this because they are a little self-indulgent. However, I decided to write it because I wanted other people to see that I have had some good times and have learnt to really make the most of them when I am feeling well.

The road trip helped clear my head, give me some fresh perspectives and come back feeling upbeat with fresh ideas about how to think creatively around the problems Poppy and I are now undoubtedly saddled with.

So off I cruised, riding dirty in my battered - and suspiciously rattling - Fiat Punto.

1. Peterborough

My first stop was Peterborough's premier Thai eatery for lunch courtesy of former Examiner reporter Andrew Jackson. The now deputy news editor at the Peterborough Evening News is one of the funniest individuals I've ever had the pleasure to work with and is the only person I know who refers to my ailment as 'disco dancer'. It was also pleasing to see his face is still substantially larger than mine.

2. Harlow, Essex

I did my post-graduate journalism course at Harlow College. I was there for six months in 2003 and took up lodgings with Horace Woolard. He is 84 and an absolute legend. It was a pleasure living with him and we would often enjoy watching the football over a glass of his home-made plum wine.

Horace and I have kept in touch over the years with Christmas cards and the odd phone call but when he heard I was ill he has been excellent at keeping in touch with both me and my family. I always said that if I was able to come down and see him I would. This sort of year has made me appreciate that too often people say they will do something like that and then never do.

I had a really good heart-to-heart with Horace. He is one of the wisest and most positive men I've ever met and he really helped me look at my latest problems with renewed energy.

He made me a cracking stew for tea and in return I took him some real ale.

3. London, South Bank

The next morning I parked the Punto and caught the train into London where I met my friend Amisha Koria. We studied physiology together at Liverpool University and we worked out we had not seen each other since my 21st birthday party.

We had a lot of fun strolling along the South Bank, catching up on all the lost years. While I was in hospital she sent me loads of fun stuff including balloons and a home made card which referred to an old joke about my slightly large hands.

4. Shaftsbury Avenue then onto Bethnal Green

Later on I met up with some of the friends I made while studying in Harlow. Many of them are now high-flyers in media or PR but still managed to come up and see me during these difficult times.

I first met up with Lucy Twitchin and Ashley Rogers and they told me tales of their glamourous lives in PR. Where Lucy works she told me they have a room that converts into a bar at certain times. The Huddersfield Examiner does not have such a room

Then me and Ash headed off to meet his wife Laura, near Brick Lane, for one of the most delicious Chinese meals I have ever tasted. There were two signs it would be good. Firstly, it was packed, secondly, it was packed with Chinese people. The food was really different to Chinese food I have tried before but the flavours were fantastic.

Ashley is a lovely bloke who really helped put my problems in perspective when I was in my isolation chamber and was raging at how his fireplace had been installed incorrectly!

5. Camden

The next day I met another Examiner old boy Richard Porritt along with his girlfriend Ellen – who used to work for our arch-rivals the Halifax Courier – and their beautiful new baby Ruby.

Porritt is now doing some great work for the Press Association and Ellen is currently on maternity leave from the Evening Standard.

It was really good seeing them both and talking about some of the old times back up in West Yorkshire. I wondered how they were coping with such hectic careers, living in London and bringing up a little one. They just seemed really happy and I don't think Ruby cried once.

It is always difficult for me thinking about having children but this meeting made me even more determined that it is something I want to do and is still, hopefully, possible.

6. Leicester Square
More friends from university and more drinks. First I met up with Megs and her boyfriend Craig before they headed off to see Mary Poppins. Then I met Ant, and his girlfriend Vicky, for a crazy Belgian meal which involved descending in a Fight Club style cage and being served by monks! Great food though.

Indie club off Oxford Road - If any of my consultants are reading this please ignore the following sentence. The steroids seem to have restored my capacity to drink lots of beer again. After that we hit some bars. I may resemble the Face of Bo, as my sister kindly suggested, but it's a small price to pay.

7. Tooting to Harlow to Northwood (Middlesex)
Got in to Ant and Vicky's flat around 3.30am Saturday, alarm went off at 8.30am and I felt surprisingly fresh.

Caught the train out to Harlow, picked up the hot wheels, and drove round to Northwood for Caroline and James' wedding. Caroline, I should point out, is Poppy's cousin.

8. Northwood to Slough
The reception was held at a beautiful location and it's fair to say it was a brilliant night. The newly weds looked fantastic and all the guests clearly had a great time.

Pops and I were seated at a table with lots of fun people. To begin with it was good thinking that none of them have seen me before so I could have a night of just being a normal guy again.

But then - what are the chances?! A 26-year-old girl next to me mentioned that she had been fighting thoracic cancer for the last year and was only just starting to return to normal life! Seriously, what are the chances? Well that was it, the cancer conversation floodgates opened. I can only apologise to everyone else on the table who had to listen to our hilarious anecdotes.

I arrived home tired but feeling much better in myself. Got the news through that I would be starting treatment later that week so just pleased to be cracking on with it. Now I am even more determined to just get through this last phase of treatment.

COMMENTS (17)

Thanks for the pie Sudders, great to see you last week. *Porritt*

Many congrats on the award - and on the riveting blog. Sorry to hear you need more treatment - what a bu55er - but hang on in there and give it all you've got. *Jill P.S. My chemo nurses think you're "cute".*

The crazy 26 year old girl from the wedding here!! Hope you are well. Thought I would have a read through your extracts, it's always interesting to get inside the thoughts of someone else sharing something similar. Even when you mentioned the dancing at the wedding, that's exactly how I felt. It puts a new spin on the 'Life is so short so dance like no one is watching' and boy did we do that partner!? Anyway, looking forward to continuing to read this and catching up soon I hope. *Lizzie*

Looks like you were busier than I was leading up to my wedding! I've always thought that being ill meant you stay in bed and moan a lot - but you have completely destroyed that stereotype! Had I not already known, I would never have guessed that you were anything but fighting fit (with a slightly larger than normal head) and I think that's amazing! It was fantastic to meet you, and I hope to see you next week for fireworks and fajitas! (If you're still taking the drugs, don't forget the alcohol!) *James*

I've been watching your story on Calendar and was touched by the way you are still so positive even after everything you have been through! You're amazing, good luck with the rest of your treatment and keep smiling! *Soph*

Hi - you don't know me but after hearing you on the radio this morning I felt compelled to come and visit your site... Although I have never been through anything like you have I have to say I found you truly inspirational, your outlook is amazing and I am sure you will have helped so many people, I wish you well for your future. I too have had to have blood transfusions and will be eternally grateful to those people who give blood. Good luck (if luck has any part to play), best wishes and here's to a long and happy future. *Bridget*

TREATING CHRONIC GRAFT VERSUS HOST DISEASE
October 26, 2007

One of the hardest aspects - after having hopefully overcome two-types of leukaemia - is explaining to people that this post-transplant complication is potentially just as life-threatening.

My new bone marrow has engrafted successfully. It is making new red blood cells, platelets and white blood cells - the cells that help fight off infection. Unfortunately, these new white blood cells are starting to attack my skin. If left alone they could attack other organs of the body including the liver and lungs.

Chronic Graft versus Host Disease (cGvHD) leads to the death of a significant number of transplant patients every year. If it can't be cured then the sufferer can be left with seriously debilitating long-term consequences.

The good news is there are a number of treatments now available. Many of them are cutting edge and more research is required to understand exactly how they work. The treatment I have just started also frankly sounds mental! It involves a kind of dialysis machine, chemicals, UV light and Rotherham.

I hope this post will explain in a bit more detail the nature of cGvHD and the treatment that offers me a 50% chance of long-term cure. On a personal note, I have to say I am worried about the future. I've just got this really bad feeling that I'm not going to fully get over this.

The full title of this entry should really be treating chronic Graft versus Host Disease (cGvHD) with Extracorporeal Photopheresis (ECP) – a headline to make even the hardiest of sub-editor clutch their stomach and wince in abject pain.

I think the best way to tackle all this is to look at all the different aspects individually.

What causes cGvHD and why does it happen?
Your immune system is designed to recognise anything that is foreign and fight it off. When I had my bone marrow transplant new cells were put into my blood. To ensure my body accepted these new cells I was prescribed a high dose of immunosuppressant drugs to stop my body attacking these new cells.

The idea was as time progresses your body learns to accept these new cells and you can taper down the dose of drugs. Frustratingly we were about two weeks away from being off the medication all together when the cGvHD flared-up.

Between 30 to 40% of transplant patients develop cGvHD and it remains one of the major challenges in the field.

It is described as being limited or extensive. If it is extensive then it can involve many organs in the body including the liver, bowels, gut and lungs. This is much harder to treat. My cGvHD, so far, appears to be limited to the skin. Limited cGvHD seems to respond better to the ECP treatment.

Another strange aspect to grapple with is that that the reaction between the newly engrafted cells and me, the host, is probably what is keeping my leukaemia at bay – or has helped see it off for good. I have a further bone marrow sample in November and because of all this remain optimistic that there should be no trace.

Why are my new cells and body reacting?
Every cell in the body wears a kind of uniform to let the immune system know what it is and what it should be doing. Think of it like a kind of hat on its surface. These are called antigens.

Even though on paper my donor was a 100% match, that is only ever as good as the technology currently available. If you were able to take a deeper look you would see that there are very slight mismatches between the make-up of my antigens and the donor's. This means there is always a risk of long-term problems.

My German donor was what is called a matched-unrelated donor but even siblings are always going to be slightly mismatched. The only perfect matches can be found in identical twins.

Conditioning
Another fascinating part of this is that the conditioning process I had to go through seems to contribute too. If you recall, in order to clear away my defective bone marrow I had to have intense chemotherapy and total body irradiation.

Research suggests that these processes can lead to two undesirable side-effects.

- It increases the number of antigens on my body's cells which will lead to a greater immune response from the newly made white blood cells.
- The processes increase inflammatory factors in my body which encourage the new white cells to attack me.

First line of treatment - steroids.
So what can be done to stop these new white blood cells giving me gip? The answer is a high-dose of steroid drugs and bumping-up the dose of immunosuppressive drugs again.

The steroids work by inhibiting the action of the new white blood cells. This stops them interacting with and damaging my body. I responded well to this treatment and incredibly my skin was entirely restored within 48 hours.

What would happen if I stopped taking the steroids now?

So why not stay on steroids for the rest of your life?

Apart from the bloating there are serious long-term problems with steroid treatment. The most dangerous aspect is that they again are stopping your immune system from working properly. This means you are at a high-risk of infection. Anyone with chicken pox, or a similarly unpleasant virus, I have to avoid literally like the plague. In fact, although cGvHD can attack other organs causing death, it is actually infection that is most likely to lead to mortality in cGvHD patients. Other long-term problems associated with steroids include:

- Osteoperosis
- Diabetes
- Mood swings
- Adrenal problems
- They can send you nuts!

How can the underlying problem be treated so that steroids can be stopped?

This is where Extracorporeal Photophoresis (ECP) comes in. In a nut shell the idea behind this treatment is that it 'turns down' the intensity of your new immune system and trains it not to attack your own body. Once this starts happening you can slowly begin to taper steroid and immunosuppressive therapy.

By the way, coming off steroids 'cold-turkey' is not advisable.

I have to say I have been amazed at what ECP entails. Extracorporeal means outside the body and photo means light. ECP therefore means light-activated treatment taking place outside the body.

The first thing to say is, despite being pretty unlucky for the last year, I have been fortunate in that Rotherham is only one of three centres that offers this treatment in the UK. Some patients have to travel down from Scotland and stop over to have their therapy.

What is ECP?
I will now be going over to Rotherham General Hospital for two three-hourly sessions, for two consecutive days, every other week.

This will initially last for three months until we know whether or not I am responding.

- A reasonably large needle is inserted into my arm (after being numbed) and I am connected to the photophoresis machine.
- About 400mls of blood is taken out of my body.

- The machine spins this blood in a special bowl. Red blood cells are heavier than white blood cells so the two can be separated.
- The white blood cells are then shipped into a special chamber where they are mixed with a chemical called Uvadex.
- Precisely how Uvadex works is not known but when it is exposed to UV light it binds to DNA in the white blood cells.
- The white blood cell layer, called a Buffy Coat, then passes over what looks like a little sun bed.
- Loss of cell viability and eventually cell death over several days.
- My red blood cells and damaged white blood cells are then returned to my body.

This all sounds a bit insane but I have to say the quality of care I have received so far has been, just like at the Hallamshire in Sheffield, absolutely excellent. The procedure is totally painless and the sisters in the department make you feel utterly at ease.

I know what you're thinking now – how the bloody hell does all this treat cGvHD? Well the honest answer is that scientists are not 100% sure. The technique was originally shown to be effective in the treatment of a type of lymphoma and subsequently other skin disorders involving a misbehaving immune system.

It was tried for patients suffering from cGvHD and seemed to work in a significant number of cases. As I said before, it is thought it could offer me a 50% chance of full recovery. However, the precise nature of this treatment remains unclear. Research continues and the Rotherham hospital's website offers some excellent information and background into the field. Teams involved with the hospital are making significant advances into understanding the whole process. **www.rotherhamhospital.trent.nhs.uk/DepartmentsServices/Photopheresis/ PhotopheresisGvHD.asp** includes a proposed model for how this treatment treats cGvHD which I thought would be a good site to include here.

- Chemotherapy and Radiotherapy (from conditioning) has caused my tissue to make more antigens on their surface.
- They also lead to more inflammatory factors being present in my body, exacerbating the problem.
- The new white blood cells being made by my new marrow don't recognise these antigens and decide to attack.
- They then create their own inflammatory products which perpetuates the problem.
- There is evidence that when the white blood cells are returned they increase anti-inflammatory factors and decrease pro-inflammatory factors.
- It also seems that they can help activate special regulatory cells that help 'train' the immune system to be more tolerant.

As I said earlier it's unfortunate this is happening to me but I'm trying to keep positive. The steroids, generally, are giving me plenty of energy so I'm trying to make the most of life while I'm feeling good. This includes trying to do a bit more work from home for the Examiner, light to medium exercise and generally enjoying myself.

I have had two sessions at Rotherham and the next pair is on November 6 and

7. I know that until at least the following sessions there will be no point in attempting to reduce the steroid dose. So, barring infection or other unforeseen complications, I should be OK for a while.

However, I am apprehensive that when the drugs are reduced problems will emerge. Like I've said so many times before all I want is to get over this and return to normal life.

Although there are other regimes doctors can try, I can't help but feel apprehensive that cGvHD will be something I have to learn to live with and manage, rather than be rid of all together. It could mean a lifetime – however long that is – of stiff joints, painful skin and general discomfort.

I hope I'm wrong.

COMMENTS (21)

My chemo nurses think you are cute, despite the steroid face! Blimey, yours is complicated! Best of luck. Stem ginger biscuits are great for the nausea. *Jill*

Remember you're not allowed to stay on the steroids forever! Being a superman isn't all it's cracked up to be, I hear! Fingers crossed for the cGvHD. Can't wait to see you both soon - get those Christmas carols at the ready! Lots of love. *H+T*

It sounds worse than RDMC versus Jason Nevins. *Toby and Sian*

Is that why you haven't had a shave - flaky face?! You'll look like a right hard nut with your bulging biceps after the steroids and your unshaven face! Chin up dude, it could be worse - you could be watching Spurs every weekend like me. *Laura*

I am very happy to have discovered your blog. What a great guy you are to share your experiences with us. My son had an unrelated matched donor transplant just over three years ago when he was 20. His original blood cancer was diagnosed in 2000 when he was 16 and went into remission after chemotherapy. However, he needed a transplant after he relapsed four years later. He has suffered from GvHD problems since his transplant and is still trying to get off the steroids. I have found the www.acor.org website, especially the GvHD mailing list to be really helpful as it puts you in touch with others dealing with GvHD. I have found your blog very helpful as it helps me realise what my son might be feeling but is unable to to express to me. I don't feel so alone after reading your blog and will post your details on the acor website because I think it will help others. *Clare*

VOTE FOR BALDY'S BLOG
November 1, 2007

Incredibly Baldy's Blog is a finalist in an international competition - the results will be announced in Las Vegas early Friday morning (UK time). Crazy isn't it?

I think the award will go to the blog with the most votes so if you have enjoyed reading my posts please get voting.

You can vote once a day. There is no prize - and it would be too risky for me to fly to America - but it sounds like fun!

Please just click on the logo and vote as much as you can. The blog is a finalist in the best medical/health issues section.

Best wishes to you all, Adrian

COMMENTS (76)

I shall be voting for you Adrian and forwarding your dad's message to all the staff at Newark High, as I have done your blogs. *Jenni*

Came across your site via the WebBlog award page. Congratulations on the nomination - you deserve it in more ways than one. From a fellow website/internet health site/admin, wish you the best in your treatment and all the best. *Garry*

I am a colleague of one of your friends, who is a physiotherapist. First of all, good luck with your further treatment of the cGvHD and your recovery of all you have been through over the last year. The blog you are writing is truly inspiring and an eye-opener. I am sure your blog will not only be a great support for cancer patients and cancer survivors, but hopefully also will make some 'healthy' people realise that they have nothing to moan about... Your story and the way it is written reminds me a bit of Lance Armstrong's book 'It's not about the bike'... I am sure you will win this year's weblog award for best medical/health issues section and many awards after this one, for many years to come. *Stefan*

Hi, used to work for your dad and have been following your rough ride for a while. Good luck for the future, keep fighting. *Lesley*

Good luck Adrian - your blog has been an inspiration to many. It has been a pleasure looking after you whilst undergoing your treatment on ward P3. *Staff Nurse Sue*

Not only did I vote, but your blog also motivated me to get on the donor register - thanks for educating us on this important issue and best of luck, both with the competition and getting better. *Anonymous*

LIVE FROM LAS VEGAS: WINNING RESULT

Because Adrian was too ill to travel, Trinity Mirror sent Steve Harrison (Web Development Manager) and Liam McNeilis (Web Content Developer) to Las Vegas for the awards. Both had been closely involved in setting up and running the blog and both were friends of Adrian.

November 9, 2007

Liam: Reporting live from The Joint in the Hard Rock Hotel, I'm at the 2007 Web Log Awards - you know, that thing Adrian had us all voting on. I'm the lucky one Adrian sent on his behalf so far that luck hasn't translated to the card tables but fingers crossed it will work for Adrian tonight and he will have won the best Health blog award.

Update at 10pm (which I think is 5am back in UK)... Adrian has won!

I'm thrilled to say that this blog is the Web Blog Awards 2007 winner. Well done to Adrian and thanks to everyone who voted.

COMMENTS (17)

Congratulations Mr Moon Face! The petitioning did the trick. If I emailed everyone and asked them to vote everyday I think I would still only have got about 20 votes so I'm mega impressed. Shame you couldn't go and shock them with your strength of 10 men drinking abilities due to the 'roids. That would have been award number 2! *Olie*

Congratulations Ade. What an amazing thing you have achieved. Let's hope that many more people will have been made aware of leukaemia and its treatment and be encouraged to join a bone marrow register or donate to a leukaemia charity to help more people with this horrible disease. *Phil*

Well done Adie! From the all the Hunter family. Fantastic news! *Ben*

Congratulations Adrian! This is really great news and I'm so pleased for you. Keep up the good work! *Julie x*

Congrats Adrian. I understand the poll was run by the same people who do the GMTV quiz questions and Blue Peter's name the cat competition. *Andrew Jackson*

Congratulations, Adrian, on a well deserved award - just sorry you can't be there in person to receive it. *Rob*

Congratulations to Adrian! A worthy winner. I knew the competition would be tough, but not exactly how tough until I read everyone else's blog… and this one deserved to win. *Lucy*

Hi Adrian, Just discovered your blog after internal company email and realised we've three things in common, we're both journalists, we both work for Trinity Mirror and sadly we're both cancer sufferers. In my case it's myeloma and I've had a stem cell transplant after high dose chemo all of which followed months of various kinds of medication including the dreaded steroids. All I can say mate is hang in there, I KNOW how hard it is and the horrors you have to deal with but it can be done. There's still ups and downs like when I got back to part-time work last year but after only a couple of weeks back collapsed in the toilet, threw up in a waste paper basket and was carried out on a stretcher in front of all my colleagues! I managed a holiday abroad early this year but had the embarrassment of feeling ill on a bus and throwing up over a German tourist! But at least I can laugh about it now and one day hopefully you will. Congrats on the award and take care. *Julian*

Hey, Adrian, congratulations, a well deserved award if ever there was one. Have you prepared your acceptance speech yet? *Jill (Oh, and my chemo nurses will want your autograph now)*

Great news! Well done. We've been looking at the graph all week and and we're thrilled for you. *Andy, Anne, Tom and Harry*

Congratulations on winning the web log award. You don't know me but I have been following your blogs for quite a while now. I have to say I think you are an amazing person and you really deserved to win the award because your blogs are educational, inspirational and a real eye opener for people. *Fiona*

Baldy's blog - truly a global phenomenon-on-on... and a well deserved winner! Well done, Sudders, catch up with you soon. *Mike*

VICTORY IN VEGAS
November 11, 2007

I still can't quite believe it, but yes, it's actually happened, I've started this entry to my leukaemia blog with the words "Yee-Ha!!!"

Baldy's Blog has now scooped an international award in the world's biggest blog competition. From Yorkshire to Las Vegas - who'd have thought it?!

A total of 545,446 votes were cast in 49 categories.

What a result and thank you so much to everyone who voted for me. Last week's voting was so much fun and a really welcome distraction. Can I just say how interesting it's been too reading some of the other blogs in my category.

If any of their authors are reading this I'm just a journalist working in Huddersfield but living in Sheffield in the UK. It's been quite an experience dipping into the world of big-time blogging. There is some really impressive stuff in our category. I wish you all continued success.

I wanted to use this post to re-cap Thursday night and try and reply to some of your fabulous comments that have been posted throughout the competition.

This award doesn't change anything for me but what it gave me, and those close to me, was a very welcome distraction for a week. That voting system was addictive wasn't it? The result has been an incredible boost. No matter what happens to me, live or die, this is something that will always be remembered and bring a smile to people's faces.

So - this is how the night unfolded.

London- time 8pm

I was invited down to London on Thursday to meet the Anthony Nolan Trust and attend a special media training day at the Groucho Club in Soho. Apparently this is quite an exclusive and famous venue but I'd never heard of it.

Throughout the day I was getting texts saying the blog was still in the lead. Then I got a call from BBC Breakfast TV asking me to come on the show the following morning. Really hoped it was going to win now.

The course finished so I tried to get a quick drink in the Groucho Club's bar - but apparently I'm not a "private member". Oh London. So I trundled off with my suitcase, hat and fat steroid head, to meet some of my friends.

By the way the steroids (also now routinely referred to as 'steds' or 'roids') are still keeping me pumped up.

I met my friends from journalism college. First up was Lucy Twitchin who showed me the famous office that transforms into a bar. I feel like I should write an entry just about how magnificent it truly is.

We then headed out to a few more bars and met Laura Oakley, Ashley Rogers and his wife Laura (you may remember them from a previous post), Will Pavia and his girlfriend Brook.

We then saw the news that some huge tidal wave was coming to wipe out the east coast of England. Sure enough, Will - who works for the Times - was called straight away to head to Norfolk.

We were all laughing because it was now a sure bet I would be ditched from the BBC's line-up. You could almost hear the national reporters grabbing their wellies, anoraks and venturing out to the action.

But we all knew that when the media gets itself really organised for a natural event that's supposed to be massive - it's rarely as exciting as it's supposed to be.

Sure enough at 9pm I was phoned and subsequently ditched from TV. The tsunami was coming! (For anyone reading this outside of the UK we were told there was going to be a huge tidal surge in the North Sea which could have flooded thousands of homes. In the end I think two cellars got a bit damp - possibly in unrelated incidents).

But I wasn't bothered - things were still looking good.

At 10pm a friend from university, Phil Driver - the guy who ran the London Marathon and raised about £5,000 for the Anthony Nolan Trust - texted to say the polls had closed and it looked like I had done it.

To celebrate my friends treated us to a bottle of Champagne.

Couldn't believe it! All we needed to hear now was the official confirmation from Liam McNeilis and Steve Harrison state-side.

Las Vegas - time (I'm a bit confused now)

Hundreds of people were gathering for the largest blog competition in the world.

Liam writes: Once again this is Liam, reporting for my good friend Adrian. I've recovered enough from both the hangover and jet lag to let you know how the awards ceremony went.

First off the award was held in 'The Joint' a nightclub within the Hard Rock Hotel. On the night before rock legend Gene Simmons from KISS played a concert here. For our night, The Joint had been hijacked by bloggers. The 2007 Blogworld Expo party and Blog Awards actually. All across America bloggers, podcasters, social networkers and assorted people who otherwise live on the internet came together for drinks, food, extremely suspicious dancing (people who live on the internet can't dance but a few brave souls did attempt to prove this theory wrong... they didn't succeed).

Of course as well as having fun the purpose of the evening was for those in the room to roar their drunken approval of each others blogs, and find out who won which awards.

The cream of the blogosphere, like everyone else, like to know who is top dog. I'm pleased to say that the top dog this year, at least in terms of Health Blogs, turned out to be our very own Adrian Sudbury. The tragedy was of course the old boy wasn't able to join us for all the free booze.

Once everyone had sampled the free grub, and more than a few free drinks, it was time for the winners to be announced. Steve Harrison did the honours and collected the award on Adrian's behalf.

Explaining that we had flown all the way from England to pick this up for Adrian, he thanked the organisers and everyone who had voted.

The organiser recommended everyone in the room to read Adrian's "inspiring" blog and privately wished us to pass on their best wishes to Adrian.

Adrian writes: If you are wondering - Liam and Steve have been incredible behind the scenes making this blog possible. I hope you all agree it looks really good, regardless of the content, and that is all down to them.

This project is not part of their job but without complaining once they have constantly updated it for me when I have been too ill. I am not a computer genius. I felt like I was in the Matrix when I cut and pasted my first bit of HTML (that is the nerdiest joke I have ever made) but any ideas I have had - problems with any pictures or videos - they have both made time to sort it out.

I was delighted when our company's top boss Sly Bailey contacted me to say that they could fly out to the awards on my behalf.

Please have a look at some of the other finalists too. I think it shows just how big and important some blogs are becoming.

Thanks once more to everyone from Huddersfield and around the world who has supported me so magnificently.

COMMENTS (6)

Reading all the blogs and comments, it is weird that the best of human nature so often comes from the worst of human circumstances. There must be a lesson in there somewhere, but for the moment I'll settle for you completing your recovery and getting back to work at the Examiner before you get too famous for us. That slightly swollen head is the steroids isn't it? *John G.*

I really like this photograph of you - can almost hear the chuckle that goes with it. It's really awesome about your blog winning. Great stuff! Hope your other treatment is going well too and that you are starting to feel almost normal now. *Anne*

SUPER STEVE HARRISON PICKS UP THE AWARD
November 13, 2007
Watch it at www/baldyblog.freshblogs.co.uk

COMMENTS (8)

Congratulations, Baldy. Sent an email to your account at the Examiner, but then it occurred to me that you might not be checking work email now. Regardless, excellent job. *Mel*

Hi Adrian, wow, just watched Vegas vid and if I'd known there was all this fame and fortune I'd have got in first with my own oldies baldy blog! (I've a bus pass by the way). Truth is I would have been too knackered both physically and mentally to do it and that's why it's brill you've had the guts to get on with it. *Julian*

I am writing from Melbourne, Australia and wanted to say this is the best information I have ever found regarding CML and the effect of a stem cell transplant. I am 38 and was diagnosed with CML two years ago and came across your blog through a posting on the CML website on yahoo only a week or so before the voting finished (You had my vote). I wanted to say I really admire what you're doing. It really does answer so many questions we all have about these diseases. Questions the doctors gloss over in so many cases. I really hope you overcome the cGvHD disease and the transplant is a cure for you. You sound like a great guy and I really do look forward to each posting. *Stef*

TREATING CHRONIC GRAFT VERSUS HOST DISEASE WITH PHOTOPHERESIS
November 19, 2007

The point of this treatment is to cure my chronic Graft versus Host Disease (cGvHD). I have around a 50% chance of it working - but I remain worried.

PS. It's been really hard convincing people that this condition is actually pretty serious!

I was back in the Sheffield hospital today for a check-up and to monitor the steroid treatment.

If you remember it's the steroids that are stopping my new immune system from attacking me at the moment. The idea is that ECP 'trains' my immune system to be more tolerant.

I was on a huge dose of a steroid called Prednisolone. To begin with it was 165mg a day. Today it has been reduced to 75mg. I'm still OK but already there are very slight areas of dry/red skin appearing. It's only very subtle but it's enough to trouble me.

As you've probably gathered the last month or so has actually been great fun. I've had some great times - that I have appreciated every second of - won awards, been out with friends, and despite a massive face and rather odd head hair, I have made the best of it.

I have also started working from home around my treatment.

The steroids have made me feel lots better and after the last year I can't tell you how good it's been being able to drink and eat like I used to. I also feel that you owe it to those who haven't been as lucky as I have to make the best of the good times you are given.

But I've always known that if the ECP doesn't work there is going to be a crunch time probably early in December.

Staying on steroids is not an option. They are stopping your immune system from working so you are at a high-risk of infection. They can also do crazy things to your body and mind.

Living with cGvHD long-term can be pretty unpleasant too. Symptoms can range from a bit of dry skin to your joints seizing up reducing your mobility. It can also spread to other parts of the body, like the mouth, making life very uncomfortable. It can affect vital organs too causing death - I'm so tired/bored of death!

Some very kind people have been in touch with the blog and let me know about their experiences. Clare let me know about a GvHD mailing list at www.acor.org. I have had a quick look today and I think it will be really useful.

I have always believed I am going to survive this episode. I have much less confidence in my quality of life being restored to normal.

COMMENTS (9)

Finally persuaded by my husband to leave you a post (on my one month married anniversary no less!). Sad to hear you a little bit down so I am reminding you that we all, and I mean WE ALL in a big way, have the utmost faith in you and your recovery. *Caromyline*

IT'S THE HAT-TRICK!

November 23, 2007

Baldy's Blog has won another award. Last night I was named feature writer of the year at the Yorkshire Press Awards.

It was a brilliant night and the Huddersfield Examiner also scooped the top award for headline of the year. It was great going out with my work friends again. Needless to say plenty of alcohol was consumed.

COMMENTS (15)

What can we say but marvellous. Big granma and I celebrated over a cup of tea this afternoon lots of love to you and Poppy. *Uncle Brian and Aunty Lucy*

THE SECOND BONE MARROW SAMPLE

November 27, 2007

I have just got back from the hospital following my second routine bone marrow sample.

It was fine, didn't hurt and is not sore at all. We were hoping to film it today but were unable to get it organised in time.

I wanted to show people that it's not a scary procedure and hoped that it might get more people thinking about bone marrow donation.

As I said before in previous posts 70% of bone marrow donation is now very similar to giving blood. Sometimes a bone marrow harvest - where it is taken from the back of the hip under a general anaesthetic - is still preferred.

What I had today with a local anaesthetic only involves one needle and a small sample is taken. The harvest uses more needles but is otherwise very similar.

Anyway, this time I'm really confident that the leukaemia won't have returned.

The chronic Graft versus Host Disease (cGvHD) has now become the main concern. Even though it is attacking my own body it should also be fighting off any residual cancer.

There will still be a two week wait to ensure both the Acute Myeloid Leukaemia and the weird chronic form I had are still in remission.

This time though I'm feeling much better about the cancer.

If it's come back this time then fair play to it!

I need to focus on the cGvHD. My hands sometimes feel hot as do my feet – both are signs that the problem persists at some level inside me.

The steroids need to be reduced as quickly as the doctors can too. My knees have started to hurt and these drugs can do long-term damage to your joints.

I've made the best of the good side-effects of the steds like being able to eat and drink again. If I'm being positive they've come at a tremendous time with all these awards nights.

I've pushed it quite a bit and loved every second of it - I don't even get hangovers!

I have also used them to try and put some muscle back on my previously emaciated frame too.

The dose was a whopping 165mg a day. Now they have been reduced to 60mg - which is still pretty high.

I am already feeling a bit more tired and there can be difficult mental side-effects coming off these drugs.

Regarding the photopheresis treatment at Rotherham we will know if that's working when the dose is dropped to about 40-50mg a day.

If it's not, all the nasty symptoms will flare up again.

By that timetable I reckon I've got another two weeks of feeling OK before crunch time.

Just hope I'm feeling good for Christmas.

In the meantime I have started working from home. The Examiner has been excellent to me and we have sorted out remote access so I can resume my role as 'digital journalist' in between my stints at hospital.

This means I am effectively editing the Examiner's website and doing bits of reporting too.

So if the site is looking terrible or a story you were in has not appeared then you know who to blame.

It's not the life I would have chosen and I have no idea what lies around the corner so planning anything is impossible.

But I've got my head round that and accepted it.

Now I just have to try and play out the cack hand I've been dealt in the best possible way.

COMMENT

Just had my ninth bone marrow test last week. Got diagnosed 19th Dec 2006 with APML a different version of AML. What a bummer!!! But I have seen loads and count myself lucky. On a research trial. Will do anything so other people do not have to go through this. Hope you are ok. *Gillian*

A NEW EXISTENCE AND MY FIRST COLD

December 5, 2007

There is no cure for the common cold so with all the bugs that are going round at the moment it was inevitable I was going to catch something.

After weeks of feeling good on the 'steds' (steroids) I am now starting the come down. Coupled with a mild cold and slight chest infection, I just feel run down and drained.

You try not to worry but it's hard not to. I know that the steroids and other drugs I am taking are stopping my immune system from working - so what exactly is going to fight this infection off?

The good news is that most colds are caused by viruses that are limited in their ability to do serious damage. Most just get into your system and burn themselves out.

But for people like me, because my body is putting up little resistance, this process can take longer and other infections can develop.

That aside the good news at the moment is I haven't got a temperature which means the infection is limited and I can continue to function as normal.

I'm writing this post while having my latest round of treatment at Rotherham.

Like I said in my previous post this is never the life I would have chosen for myself. But with the help of my ever-supportive colleagues at the Huddersfield Examiner I have started to carve out a new existence.

I have now reprised my role as 'digital journalist' which means I am effectively editing the Examiner's website. My job is to put on any breaking news, ensure all the stories are in the right sections and edited correctly along with selecting pictures to illustrate articles on the web.

The role also means I should be trying to encourage more people into the site through the forums - and blogs.

When I talk about living a new life I also mean accepting that you can no longer plan ahead. I initially found this incredibly difficult - my life plan was that around about now I would have been working for a national news operation in London.

That's what I planned but things change. Now I'm just grateful that I still have a job and that once again I've got a useful function.

Resuming my role frees up an extra reporter in the office which for regional papers is invaluable.

I should add at this point a big thank you to fellow Examiner reporter Sam Casey who has been covering me for the best part of a year.

It's fair to say he was mildly pleased when the remote kit arrived and I was able to work from home.

The steroid dose continues to be reduced so, again, we will have no idea how I'm going to be until the next couple of weeks have passed.

But I have accepted that now. I have sort of trained myself not to think too far ahead. I have work to keep me busy along with as many little projects on the side as I can come up with.

This is coupled with taking Poppy out whenever we are able, seeing friends and family and generally trying to have a good time.

My new attitude also means I don't get scared or inhibited like I used to. If I think something needs saying then generally I will say it.

One of my biggest fears used to be public speaking. I'm still not good at it but I've been asked to talk in front of hundreds of people at several big charity events now and I'm just not phased by it. I suppose living with death hanging over you for so long has to have some hardening effects.

I also find myself very intolerant of people who moan about things that simply do not matter.

I still hate the fact my face is bloated and again my hair has changed - it's come back thick and dark. It's about two steps away from an afro. The 'steds' have also changed the rate at which my hair grows so its receding patches are accentuated.

When I look in the mirror I don't see me looking back which is quite difficult.

I think that's why I still like wearing my hat. I can imagine Trinny and Susannah saying it helps detract from my engorged head.

But the new me doesn't care that much.

At the Yorkshire Press Awards it was a black-tie do and I decided to keep my hat on just because I wanted to.

I would never have done that a year ago.

I'm sure some people will have thought I looked like a right plonker but I genuinely was not concerned.

A 50% CHANCE OF DYING! I'M NOT HAVING THAT - IT'S NEARLY CHRISTMAS
December 10, 2007

So it turns out the cold was a little bit more serious than first thought.

Here I am again, having a cup of tea – and some more treatment - back in the Royal Hallamshire hospital.

My cold-like symptoms are actually being caused by a virus called Respiratory Syncytial Virus (RSV). In most people it just gives them a nasty cough and cold.

Their immune systems will usually take care of it unassisted within a few weeks.

But for people like me, who are pumped up on steroids along with other immunosuppressants, the situation can be much more serious. If the infection takes hold and spreads it can cause pneumonia or bronchiolitis.

One of the doctors told me that in these cases mortality can be as high as 50% - crumbs!

I'm sure I'm going to be OK though – only 50%? I ridicule those odds.

When I reported my cold last week to the staff on P3 day ward they go through the following tests:

- Listen to the lungs and chest.
- X-ray my chest to see if there is any sign of infection.
- Get me to produce a sputum (phlegm) sample.
  Interesting point: When I was in hospital for my main stay I asked the nurses whether it was patient urine or faeces that they hated dealing with most and they nearly all said it was sputum they disliked above all else.
- An NPA (Nasal Pharyngeal Aspirate) - this is horrible. They shove a tube right up, and I mean right up, the back of your nose and suck. This hunts for any viruses.

The sputum and contents from the NPA are sent off to the labs. Samples are taken and an attempt is made to grow, or culture, any bacteria or viruses that might be living there, and identify them.

On Saturday evening I got a call from the P3 team that virologists had detected RSV.

I have to say at this point a big thank you to everyone working behind the scenes in these labs. I know a few of you have been following the blog and just wanted to say that you have all helped save my life - along with hundreds of other patients - several times over this year.

Your work has meant doctors have been able to administer the correct antibiotics, or in this case antiviral treatments, as quickly as possible, which as you know is so crucial in keeping people like me alive.

Antibiotics are only effective against bacterial infections.

Viruses are generally a little trickier hence why there is no cure for the common cold.

But, luckily for me, RSV can be treated by inhaling an antiviral agent called Ribavirin.

Every other day I'm also having infusions of a substance called Immune Globulin which is supposed to boost my compromised immunity.

The reason I am so confident of getting over this little problem is because I still feel well, it's been caught early and I feel like I'm improving already.

My symptoms, as I described last time, involved feeling a bit run down coupled with an irritating cough. The only weird thing was that sometimes when I inhaled I could hear my chest crackling. It sounded a bit like a frog's croak.

Other than that I've had no fevers so the infection, thankfully, looks limited.

If people are ill around you at the moment, with similar symptoms to these, it is quite likely their cold is being caused by RSV. It's doing the rounds and for most of you it will clear up in a couple of weeks.

The only downside to this latest – but almost inevitable – setback is it's just really inconvenient.

Work was going great from home and I was doing gentle exercise again. I was just trying to build up some sort of routine in an otherwise unpredictable life.

My colleagues have been great and will pick up my work again but I feel bad because it just means they have more work to do in already busy days.

The problem for me is that I need to have treatments at 8am, 2pm and 8pm each day for about another five days.

Each one lasts for two hours with a break in between. People shouldn't really come in the room while the Ribavirin is pumping out – it's not good for pregnant women or healthy lungs – and because I've got an infectious disease I shouldn't really be leaving my room and putting other patients at risk.

That said, there's a couple of patients on here with TB who apparently keep popping out of their rooms which if you ever needed an incentive not to leave your room that's as good as any.

So effectively I'm stuck here with no visitors and the mask makes phone calls a little tricky too.

Yesterday I pleaded with the doctors to let me go home at 10pm to which they agreed as long as I was feeling OK and my oxygen levels remained high.

It's not ideal but I found the break really helped.

I had started to feel a bit sick, the first time for months, and all the difficult emotions of being in isolation started to creep back into my mind.

It's just the little things like having to eat hospital food when they bring it to you, the sweaty condensation that drips from the blue covers that keep it warm, nurses walking in when you're taking a leak, the needle in your arm coming loose and catching on your clothes, trying to negotiate your way around the room when connected to a drip stand - just being lonely and having nothing to do.

I started thinking about sadder times and lost friends. It was as though the balloon of the last three steroid-fuelled months had well and truly burst into deflated strips of dishevelled and broken colours.

Going home was the best thing for me. It allowed me to snap out of this mood and buck my ideas up. Today I've come back in armed with laptop, books, a few arm weights and a list of jobs to do.

Thank God I've got this blog to write too!

COMMENTS (19)

I don't really know what to say. I just began reading your blog last week and find you to be the most inspiring person I know. You make my self pity and complaints go away. You made me open my eyes and see things from a whole new perspective. One with much more gratitude than ever before. Thank you for that. Your positive attitude is contagious. Thank you for keeping a blog of your journey. I wish you all the best for a quick and speedy recovery. *Hollie*

You're allowed to feel down from time to time you know. It's not a sin, but glad to hear you're once again, amazingly, bouncing back. What an inspiration. *Jill*

OUT AGAIN AND REPLIES TO READERS
December 18, 2007

Just been discharged and it's great to be out.

Even though the cough hasn't entirely gone it's much better than it was before and I'm assured that the treatment has probably got rid of the virus.

The doctors told me that it is likely I'm no longer infectious and the cough will just work itself out.

It's really strange getting a viral infection like this and knowing I have not got an immune system to deal with it.

The advice, as ever, remains if it gets worse - come back in.

I really hope it doesn't. I've got more pressing matters to attend to including a bit of last minute Christmas shopping and spending lots of time over the festive period with Poppy, my family, her family and friends.

Two difficult issues remain nibbling at the back of my mind though.

Still not heard back from my latest bone marrow sample and we are approaching crunch time to find out just how much of a problem Graft versus Host Disease is going to be.

COMMENTS (9)

Great news! Our fingers are crossed that you're going to stay healthy! *Jen*

Great to hear you are home ! You were pushing us over the 250 gifts - but we don't mind the extra wrapping for our fave reporter! *Anonymous*

A BLOODY MYSTERY, SALAD DAYS AND PORK PIES
December 21, 2007

The equivalent of around three bags of blood has gone missing from my body.

Needless to say this came as a bit of a shock yesterday.

Since being discharged from hospital on Monday with the viral chest infection I've been feeling a little drained and run down.

I also found it hard walking to the shops without getting out of breath.

But I just assumed all this was down to my body slowly recovering.

On Thursday I came back over to Rotherham hospital to continue with the Photopheresis treatment for Graft versus Host Disease.

Blood samples were taken but the levels of my haemoglobin – the substance which carries oxygen around the body – came back alarmingly low.

And it was all going so well too!

Once again I was being taken really good care of by the staff in their festive attire. Tea, biscuits – even a fresh fruit salad with cream was knocked up at one point. Salad days indeed!

But then those numbers came back.

Any leukaemia patient will tell you that they become obsessed with their 'counts' – the measure of how well their bone marrow is performing.

I described all this in previous posts but if I am to be grateful for anything it's that post transplant my new bone marrow has been producing healthy levels of red blood cells (which contain haemoglobin), platelets (which stop you bleeding to death) and white cells.

It's one aspect of my treatment that has not been a problem.

Normal levels of haemoglobin in healthy males range between 13 and 18 (grammes per 100 millilitres). Mine had been stable at around 12 for weeks so I've not really had to think about it.

But from Monday to Thursday it had dropped from close to 12 to just over 8.

That's a lot in a very short space of time.

Just as a rough guide, a hospital bag of blood (around 300mls) will boost your haemoglobin count by one – so you can imagine how difficult trying to get by with the best part of a litre missing can become.

As I've said before (God, I'm tedious) my background is physiology and I know that even if this drop was attributed to the infection it's just too much to lose over that time period.

Frankly, I was cacking it.

So what else could have caused it?

The answer, it seems, lies with the Ribavirin therapy I received to treat the chest infection. One of the side-effects listed for some patients is haemolysis – the breaking down of red blood cells.

When this was explained to me I did feel a little more at ease because at least there seemed to be a logical reason behind what was happening.

I could also understand that a couple of bags of blood would be a good solution and should see me right for Christmas.

But now a bigger problem emerged - when was I going to pick up my pork pies?

It's so difficult sometimes living your life from week to week, never knowing what lurks around the corner and being unable to make any firm plans.

I have tried to embrace this new existence so no longer get annoyed when the plans you do make have to go out of the window yet again.

Immediately when faced with these snags my brain now turns to how they can be worked around.

For example, today I had to finish off some Christmas shopping in Sheffield and then head over to Gordon Dyson's butchers in Shepley, Huddersfield, to pick up some magnificent pork pies. They are amazing if you haven't tried them.

The original plan was to have the photopheresis and then complete all those tasks later in the afternoon. Get home and pick up Poppy from her work's do - also in Rotherham.

The counts were too low for photopheresis treatment this morning so kindly the staff at Rotherham ordered me up two bags of blood - which I know from previous experience takes quite a few hours.

This gave me enough time to shop and then return to Rotherham for the transfusions.

Each bag takes around two hours so I should be done by 7pm. I decided writing this would help pass some time while my new A+ blood drips slowly into me.

The transfusions should boost my energy levels and make me feel tons better. My counts should also improve so that I can come in to complete the second photopheresis treatment in the morning.

Please nothing else before Christmas!

COMMENTS (10)

A butchers in Shepley. My my, how you've changed. What's up with that farm shop in Netherton you turncoat. *Andrew*

MERRY CHRISTMAS TO EVERYONE!
December 25, 2007

Just a quick post to let everyone know Poppy and I are engaged!

I asked her to marry me after midnight mass and she said yes. I know I'm not a great investment but it just felt like the right thing to do.

It was a brilliant Christmas Eve and we had loads of friends round at my parents' house in Pinxton, Nottinghamshire.

Joining me and Pops were my mum and dad, my sister Carrie, and my best man Ben Hunter.

I have no idea what this year holds - and no idea about wedding plans - but I know if I can last until the summer it will be a fantastic do.

Once again wishing all readers a very Merry Christmas.

COMMENTS (35)

Once again Adie displays great courage in selecting me as his best man! I have entered into a strict training regime to end my chaotic and disorganised ways. I feel hugely honoured to have been asked to be best man. All the Pinxton lot send their congratulations, once again a toast to Adie and Poppy! *Ben*

Congratulations Adrian & Poppy!!! *Anonymous*

Right Aido, the footy lads are thinking about a stag do!! Congratulations to you both, you made my Christmas with that news. *Gavo*

CRUNCH TIME

Happy New Year to everyone and thank you for all your lovely comments.

After a wonderful Christmas and New Year it's sadly back to business and in the next couple of weeks we should know how effective the photopheresis at Rotherham has been in treating the chronic Graft versus Host Disease (cGvHD).

The steroid taper is rapidly approaching crunch time.

If the treatment hasn't been successful the unpleasant problems associated with cGvHD will reappear.

These could include:

• Incredibly dry skin
• Impaired joint mobility
• Unbearable itchiness

The bad news is that some of these symptoms, albeit in a very mild form, have started to emerge already.

I'm convinced that cGvHD is something I will have to live with for the rest of my life.

The question is just how debilitating it will be.

The sad thing about reducing the steroid dose is that I'm no longer bristling with energy, but I have still got an oversized head.

The side effects do reverse once you're off the drugs but why couldn't I keep the va va voom and ditch the pumpkin with a neck? My future father in law remarked over Christmas that I resembled a hamster! And he's not wrong. It's like having two golf balls shoved up in my cheeks.

It is also worth being aware of the irony that although the cGvHD could go on to ruin my life, it's probably saved my life by fighting off any remaining leukaemia.

I wanted to write an update about where I am at with the 'sted' reduction.

To begin with the dose was dropped by about 10mg a week. Now I'm down to 25mg a day and the next reduction will be in steps of 5mg.

However, not only do I need to be weaned off those drugs but also the other immunosuppressant I take which is called ciclosporin.

In an ideal world I will be able to come off the steroids then begin a taper for the ciclosporin.

Once I'm off both drugs - and no longer have any cGvHD because it's been cured by the photopheresis - my new immune system will be able to function and I will be able to return to my normal life.

Unfortunately I just don't believe that's going to happen.

I've now met people like me whose lives involve a never ending cycle of cGvHD flaring up, which is brought under control with a high dose of steroids, which in turn brings with it the high infection risk - and the huge face.

Over Christmas I was fortunate enough to avoid any major infections but I still feel under the weather and there are a few problems with my chest.

The doctors say it sounds clear and I'm taking both antibiotics and antivirals so I should be OK but I'm struggling with my energy levels.

It's really hard to know if this is due to an infection, whether it's my body just recovering from the pre-Christmas infection or if it's the chemical come down associated with coming off the steds.

It is also terrifying reading about all these bugs, like norovirus, doing the rounds. I'm really grateful that I can stay in my flat and work on the Examiner's website from home.

Do you remember a comedy on BBC2 called Game On? I feel like the dude with the surfboard. Never mind!

I have no idea what 2008 holds but with a wedding to organise for August there is certainly plenty to keep me distracted.

COMMENTS (10)

I check the blog every couple of days to see if you've posted and see how you are. A big congrats for your engagement and cheers to a fab August wedding. I really hope all goes well coming off the steds and the cGvHD doesn't reappear. *Stef*

A TRIBUTE TO DONNA
January 10, 2008

I have had a day of very mixed emotions.

My job involves editing the Huddersfield Examiner's website and today's front page article involved Dr Donna McCormick a clinical psychologist who lost her battle against leukaemia.

Dr McCormick was diagnosed with acute lymphoblastic leukaemia in February 2007.

I have spoken to Donna's mum and emailed her husband Greg.

I just wanted to say again to Donna's family that I am thinking about you all at this very difficult time and thank you for all your kind words.

BAD NEWS BUT DON'T WORRY TOO MUCH
January 18, 2008

Just found out that the chronic myeloid leukaemia could be back.

I couldn't believe it when my doctor revealed the results of my second bone marrow sample. I was just so confident it would still be a total remission.

However, I am not too worried about it.

As a journalist you are trained to put the most interesting facts at the top of the story. The purpose of this is to grab the reader's attention and make them want to read on.

I hope that's been achieved.

Now, before I explain why it's important not to be too concerned at this stage, please permit me a little bit of whinging.

The news from the hospital the other day was hugely disappointing. I came home without saying much and just cracked open a couple of beers.

Sometimes I'm not sure who to turn to.

What should I say and how do I expect this person to reply? It's clearly not all going to be all right.

At the time I couldn't really explain how I was feeling but now, after reflecting and putting together this entry, I think I understand.

Strangely enough this blog is evolving into my own coping strategy - something I never intended it to be in the beginning.

My response to the news had been one of bitter acceptance but I was really apprehensive about telling my family. I am tired of upsetting people I love and it's quite draining going through the same complicated haematology several times over.

Also a dark cloud, that for a time had seemed distant, was once more in the foreground and looming ominously.

The crux of the matter is that, like Hitler in the latter stages of World War Two, I am just fighting on too many fronts;

- Chronic Graft versus Host Disease - which I know is going to flare up again. My hands and feet feel like they're burning some days and my skin is a little itchier. Steroids are down to 20mg a day.
- Constant infection risk.
- Because of the radiotherapy and the cGvHD my eyes are getting drier. I know they will probably require operating on to treat cataracts later this year.
- Coping with my big face and boggly eyes.
- Infertility and IVF.
- Thinking about the long-term future.
- Organising a wedding (which is quite fun actually).
- And now the prospect of leukaemia again.

It's like I'm walking through a minefield - which ever way I turn I encounter difficulties.

I don't think I'm scared I just feel angry at this increasingly impossible situation I have ended up in.

Now for the good news.

My bone marrow is essentially very healthy. It's making all the cells it's supposed to and in all the correct numbers.

The other tests carried out on my bone marrow came back clear with the exception of one.

This molecular test is really sensitive and it only gives a yes or no answer. It showed that there is a protein present in my marrow associated with CML.

My consultant, who was really good and had obviously spent time making sure he gave me the facts without causing me to be too alarmed, explained that the results of this test are hard to interpret.

Firstly, it is really sensitive and the result could have come from background noise or interference.

Secondly, if the cancer is making a comeback my situation means I have a very good chance of fighting it off:

- I have started taking the 'miracle drug' Glivec again. In recent years it has transformed the treatment of patients with CML. For many it represents a cure or at least holds the leukaemia at bay for many years.
- As my cGvHD almost inevitably revs up again that will also play a role in attacking any cancerous cells. With a bit of luck my new immune system will recognise any cells associated with CML as being foreign, kill them, without bothering the rest of my body too much.

What reassured me most was when my consultant said that on an anxiety scale - with 0 being nothing to worry about and 10 being soil your pants - he rated this situation somewhere around 1.5.

If you get your head round the science I'm sure he's correct.

He also said because of the Glivec and cGvHD there is every chance the results could be all clear following my next bone marrow test in April.

I was a bit down after hearing the news but I'm OK again now. Nothing has changed, plus I'm still alive and relatively well.

Apologies for such a downbeat entry because I had planned to do something much more entertaining.

I promise next week's will be more fun - although as this week shows you never know what's around the corner.

COMMENTS (32)

Sorry to hear about the possibility that CML has returned. Glivec is a wonder drug and has worked for many people who have had years on it... You have been through such a lot, you deserve some good luck now. You will get it... Arrange your wedding to Poppy, carry on as normal, you know that we are all behind you 100%. *Dawn*

This can only be a minor setback for a major person! All the Catch family are holding you, in our thoughts. By the way, Gordon the butcher reckons a pie or two should be part of the treatment! *Catch*

Keep going mate. Your sense of perspective and bottle is humbling. *Greg*

BALDY'S 500TH COMMENT
February 1, 2008

A video of Adrian dancing to celebrate the 500th comment posted on Baldy's Blog, which Adrian wanted to be a big thank you to everyone out there. Liz Boffey was the 500th comment. He celebrated it in typical form with party hats, hooters and a very strange piece of dancing.

COMMENTS (30)

Congrats on 500! Enjoyed browsing your site. Best wishes with your battle. You're in my prayers. *Chip*

I can't believe I'm the official 500th comment - what an honour and a privilege. Like you, I feel this blog has taken on a life of its own. *Liz*

You've got to do the Dirty Dancing first dance. The way you bust a move cries out Swayze to me! Love it! *Michelle*

GRAFT VERSUS HOST WITH THE MOST
February 18, 2007

It's back.

The steroid dose is now down to 12.5mg a day and the chronic Graft versus Host Disease (cGvHD) has started to bubble up to the surface of my skin.

The affected areas at the moment are my thighs and elbow pits. It's a horrible experience, but bearable. At this stage I think it can still be managed by moisturisers and steroid cream.

What is difficult to deal with is that I know it's only going to get worse.

The treatment at Rotherham may have helped but it certainly has not cured me.

The pessimist in me would be keen to point out that I'm actually worse off today than I was before my bone marrow transplant.

Now I've got leukaemia, cGvHD, a terrible immune system, normal energy levels and a head like a Space Hopper.

But of course on the plus side I'm not dead.

I know I am a positive person but sometimes I think a break wouldn't be too much to ask for.

What I am also coming round to accept is that this is something I will NEVER recover from.

These red patches on my thighs are only going to spread and get worse as the steroids reduce further.

I suspect my skin could eventually break down like it did before.

It's dangerous to stay on these drugs long-term and from a vanity point of view I have always tried to have a laugh about my bloated appearance but on the inside it is getting me down.

During the last four months I have met, or heard from, lots of people who live with cGvHD around the world and it can be a pretty miserable or challenging existence.

Many are never able to return to work, and if they do, just get struck down with serious infections.

In some, cGvHD spreads to other organs like their eyes, lungs, liver and gut.

It can be unbearably itchy, sore and hugely debilitating.

Not bad for a condition hardly anyone has heard of.

For me the skin around my legs is really tight. It's like walking on two tubes.

It's not too painful but jogging and walking, especially uphill, is very difficult.

Have you ever been in the sea then dried your legs off in the sun? Sometimes my legs feel like a more uncomfortable version of that.

Other times it's more like mild sunburn and at the moment it appears to be flaring up then dying down across different areas of the body.

My plan was always to make a full recovery, get back to work and start playing football again.

Now I just don't think it's ever going to happen.

Having your own immune system nibble away at you from the inside is a very unpleasant concept, not least because there is nothing I can do to stop it.

On a lighter note, I have always liked to think of myself as a metro-sexual kind of guy, someone who is down with my female friends and readers.

So this last picture is for you sisters:

The steroids have actually given me stretch marks.

COMMENTS (33)

You need a powerful moisturiser. In the States, we were recommended "UDDERly sMOOth", which is actually intended for cows with sore teats but is the best moisturiser money can buy! *Roobeedoo.* **Adrian replies:** Morning Roobeedoo. That product sounds incredible. Soothing cows' teats - are you winding me up?! I am tempted to say, "Pull the udder one..."

Overcoming the mountain of the BMT only to find yourself now battling with the cGvHD must feel incredibly tough - not to mention unfair. To acknowledge your enemies is to stare them in the face, and that takes just as much courage as staying positive. *Pru*

No PICTURES OF MY ARSE THIS WEEK AND CAN YOU HELP WITH A LITTLE DILEMMA?

March 6, 2008

Plunged into despair, buoyed by incandescent hope, crushed by another setback, fighting illness and misery from all quarters, stuck in an impossible situation yet life remains rich with possibility; determined not to let this disease beat me.

What a pretentious gob shite.

Now let's get down to business.

The chronic Graft versus Host Disease (cGvHD) is back under control and the steroid dose has been reduced to 10mg a day. So far there has been a slight rash and my skin is a little drier but nothing else.

I also have stopped needing to go to the toilet in the middle of the night. Bonus.

What is important for people to understand is that some sufferers from cGvHD NEVER make a full recovery. This condition wrecks lives and if it is really debilitating can make your life beyond miserable.

I've heard tales from many people, while being treated at Rotherham, and from around the globe thanks to a cGvHD mailing list and you realise it's rather depressing stuff.

Endless cycles of steroids, immune system suppression, infection and very unpleasant complications.

And of course no one's heard of cGvHD - loads of people give you sympathy when you've got leukaemia!

But bear in mind a small amount of this bloody thing will actually stop the cancer returning. One fellow cGvHD sufferer, who has lived for years after his transplant and still going strong, says he has actually come to love his cGvHD for that very reason.

I had a very positive meeting with my consultant at Rotherham yesterday.

He says he is determined to get me off the steds and that my face should start deflating at doses below 10mg. Not an actual quote.

Learning more about the nature of cGvHD is also interesting.

He describes it as an 'undulating ocean with peaks and troughs'.

Imagine the steroid dose as being a line that increasingly approaches the peaks of the waves.

As the dose drops further, the wave tips start to burst through the steroid line, and you can see this on the surface of your skin.

The disease will naturally rise and fall in a cyclical pattern.

I need to learn what is 'normal' for me and spot it before it spirals hideously out of control.

It seems to move around the body and affect different people in different ways.

For example the hairs on my legs have all but gone yet my arms remain ape-like.

My consultant explained that cGvHD can hit the scalp too and cause permanent hair loss there due to scarring and damage of the hair follicles.

Why this all happens, and why different people are affected so differently, remains a mystery.

As for me here is a real life dilemma.

I would really value your opinions on this one.

I'm in a great position at the moment in that I can work from home but still have time to exercise and look after myself.

If I was a teacher or builder with cGVHD this would be much harder.

A job has come up at the Huddersfield Examiner (the paper I work for) which is basically head of multi-media. If it wasn't for cGvHD it would be the perfect promotion for me.

Here are some of the cool things we've done with the site since I got back to work:

www.examiner.co.uk/leisure-and-entertainment/unsigned-bands

http://huddersfieldfresh.ning.com

www.examiner.co.uk/travel-news/ex-pats

The job would be really challenging and I've got lots to offer.

The money would also help considerably what with me and Pops looking to marry and buy a house.

But the job needs someone to be in the office - which I understand. The reason I have only had one major infection since November is because I have been so sensible in staying at home.

The other point, which I have talked to the editor about, is that I could get taken seriously ill at any point and be away from work for weeks - if not longer.

And then there is also the possibility of the leukaemia coming back.

My current position allows me to fit work around treatments whereas in the new role that would be a bit more difficult.

Trinity Mirror (the company I work for) have been tremendously supportive to me throughout my illness and I don't want to take on a job that I am unable to give 100% to.

I would be interested to know what you all think.

Finally a big shout out to the journalism students at Sheffield College.

I was asked to go along and speak to them the other day about blogging and online journalism.

When I was at journalism college in Harlow we had a sub-editor from the Mirror come in and talk to us so I hope they weren't too disappointed when old fat head rolled into their classroom.

COMMENTS (24)

It's a difficult one to call. My gut feeling is if you're well enough at the moment is to give it a go and I'm sure your work mates and colleagues will understand if it doesn't work out as you plan. *Julian*

That job sounds great, I can't really add any more to what everyone else has said… it's a tough call with the infection risk, but I reckon if you're feeling strong and able to perhaps have a trial run, you should go for it! *Catherine*

I think you've done so well so far why risk the chance of infection. *Rachel*

GRAFT VERSUS HOST FLARE AND CONTINUED STEROID TAPER
March 21, 2008

Think this post illustrates just what a knife edge people with chronic Graft versus Host Disease - and who are trying to come off their steroids - are really on.

I am now on 10mg a day. If it wasn't for the sted face I would happily stick now. Yikes!

It was really bad. My skin felt hot all the time and it was starting to get itchy. I hammered it with steroid creams and moisturisers but it didn't seem to be shifting.

I even used "Udderly Smooth" which turns out is actually a real product! Thanks for that suggestion.

The flare also seemed to make me feel really tired.

I've always been able to keep my spirits up, but when this happened I just felt crushed. I thought we had come as far as possible and I would have to accept looking like this for the rest of my life.

It wouldn't be so bad but every time I see myself it's a reminder of everything that's happened to me and a reminder that I am still ill.

Mercifully two days later it was better.

It was completely back to normal.

This condition is so strange. Now I just want to try 5mg and hope for the best.

COMMENTS (11)

I'm sure that it must be depressing and disconcerting to look at yourself and see someone "different", but as someone who's only seen you through videos, the sted face isn't off-putting. If I walked by you on the street I don't think I'd even notice. Small comfort, I know, but at least you're not scaring dogs and small children. *Jen*

You know you're always gorgeous to me - I just can't wait for you to get rid of the damn hat! *Helen*

THE PUNTO IS DEAD - LONG LIVE THE VECTRA. PLUS 5MG OF STEDS A DAY AND A MORE SERIOUS FLARE
April 1, 2008

I must begin this post with some more sad news.

My much loved N-reg Fiat Punto has died. I had come to think of it as the Herbie of the leukaemia world.

Time of death 3pm, Tuesday, March 31, 2008.

Location: M1 northbound just short of Woolley Edge services between junctions 38 and 39.

RIP little guy.

Above: From left, me as an elf, my best mate Ben as a clown and my sister Carrie in normal 80's attire. This was taken during some production at John King Infant School, Pinxton. Given the nature of the outfits I can only assume it was the Nativity Play or the Passion of the Christ.

Above: Me and my lovely sister on holiday in France. Look at that flowing and beautiful hair. She must have been jealous.

Right: My dad Keith, oh yes he is called Keith, and me exchanging a macho moment in the south of France. I hope you are all enjoying the hair evolution. By this stage it had moved on from the ill-judged under cut.

Below: Great days at Liverpool University clubbing at the famous Blue Angel or Raz nightclub. Can't remember why we were overdressed but having another excellent night. Mates, from left, Tom Ward, Andrew McDonough and Phil Driver.

Above: Interviewing Anne Widdicombe. Had about five minutes to prepare for the interview so quickly glanced on Wikipedia. Asked her if she agreed with the online statement about her being a gay icon. It didn't go down too well. Otherwise I genuinely thought she came across well.

Left: Hammering the phones on another hot scoop. Hounding down rogue builders, outing local Tory party bullies, exposing international charity scams - or just stunting up a picture for photographic. Give them another job to moan about.

Right: I love the fact that despite being no oil painting I can actually say that I was once a model, for a Huddersfield Examiner fashion shoot. I suppose it counts. I only got the gig because no one else in the office was up for it. Found it surprisingly enjoyable although there is never an excuse for the white plimsoll/suit combo.

Right: Minus the hair and at my lowest weight. Before I was taken ill I weighed a healthy 83kg. This was how I looked after my second cycle of chemotherapy. I weighed just above 70kg. It also shows what it is like to live with a Hickman Line. This makes receiving chemo, blood, fluids and antibiotics so much easier. It means you don't have to be stabbed every day either to get your blood counts.

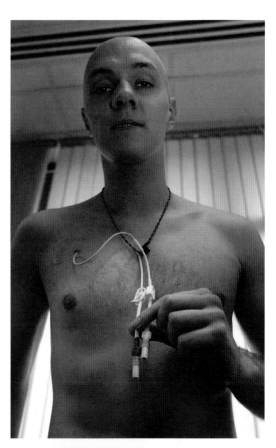

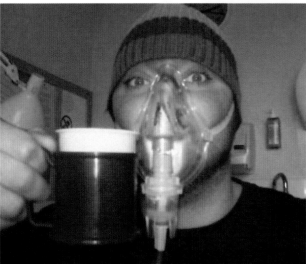

Left: Being treated for a serious respiratory virus (RSV) before Christmas 2007. Raising a toast - there was no way I was going to miss another Christmas. I was determined to get out of there and ten days on and off a nebuliser did just that.

Above: Back in the office and saying hello to all my friends. Natural shot of me reading the paper like we all do every day. One of my favourite comments from fellow reporter Andrew Jackson: "If I'm not on the front or page three; I'm not interested."

Right: Me and Natasha Kaplinsky. She was lovely and really took an interest in the story and our campaign. Spent lots of time talking to her both on and off air.

Above: Outside Westminster meeting with Health Secretary Alan Johnson.

Above: I think this is one of Gordon Brown's best pictures ever taken. Doesn't he look cheerful? Really enjoyed talking to him and he gave me a good 20 minutes. One to one he was an excellent communicator and our conversation ranged from football through to all the issues I wanted to raise. When the press came in at the end you could see his huge intellect taking over and thinking too much about where his hands should be and how the press could spin this situation. He struck me as genuine and someone who really wanted to help.

10 DOWNING STREET

THE PRIME MINISTER

Dear Adrian

It was great to meet. You show inspirational courage to us all. Please send me my letter you want passed on and I will help you with your campaign. We are all thinking of you

Gordon

Right: Letter written with "Gordon's Crayon" - ask Kali for full story!

Left: At my Sheffield flat having a meal and a few glasses of wine with my family.

Above: On holiday in the apartment in the south of France I hope my parents will eventually move out to for good. I love this picture. Me and Carrie in the middle with my mum Kay and dad Keith.

Of course my old car giving up the ghost wouldn't normally feature in my leukaemia blog but it's such a strange story I thought I had to include it.

My friends and family all knew the Punto well.

It had done the best part of 114,000 miles carrying me and many others all over the country.

Fans of this blog will recall me 'riding dirty' in my Punto on my road trip in November.

Despite much love for these wheels I'd been planning to get a new car for ages. I managed to save a bit of money last year and, along with some cash from the awards, I bought a 2005 Vauxhall Vectra.

The deal was done last week and the Punto was to be part exchanged - basically £75 for scrap.

So yesterday I finished my work for the Examiner and headed up the M1 to Dewsbury. About five miles into the journey I noticed the car was losing power.

I shifted down into fourth gear and managed to maintain a good 60mph.

Then smoke started to appear from the exhaust and I knew it was terminal.

My speed dropped again so I slammed it into third.

The engine screamed - so I turned the radio up. That didn't help. I was only about 15 miles away so if I could just keep going…

By this time I was doing 40mph and so much smoke was pouring out the rear that I was becoming a serious hazard.

Lorries were overtaking me but the final straw was when a caravan sped by.

I spluttered onto the hard shoulder, opened the bonnet, only to be greeted by a huge amount of steam.

It was like something from a cartoon.

When it was safe I peered in again and engine oil was splattered everywhere. The head gasket had gone and there was no way it could have been fixed without incurring a huge bill.

It was almost like the Punto knew it was its last trip.

Anyway, I then had to get a breakdown crew to tow me to the garage in order to complete the part exchange.

For someone who has not had the best of luck recently I have to say that was incredible. The car was brilliant for pottering around Sheffield and had really served me well.

It will never be forgotten.

Anyway my new car is boss. It's so good being able to drive above 60mph and not be genuinely scared of dying in an horrific metal mangle.

It looks cool too and it's got a CD player.

Anyway, enough of that.

My steroid dose is now down to 5mg a day (remember it was 165mg to begin with).

That's the sort of dose normal people are given if they have inflammation problems.

I've been at that dose for over a week now and am currently experiencing what I hope is a flare.

The skin on my body is fine but my face is really red.

It's also still massive - why? Deflate, damn it! Come on!

Last night my stomach was unwell and I had the runs too. This was really worrying because it could mean the graft versus host disease has spread to the stomach and gut.

Thankfully today it seems better so I'm less concerned.

My shins are quite itchy too.

There has been a flare at every steroid dose since 10mg and my skin has always come back under control.

I just hope it is the same this time.

On another note I found out today I didn't get that job.

If I was the editor it was exactly the same decision I would have made. I'm just unable to commit to the office hours.

I would have loved the job but this morning when I woke up shattered, bricking it and with a face hotter than my ex-Punto's head gasket, the last thing I would have wanted to do is drive to some conference or do a full day's work in an office environment.

COMMENTS (23)

Just wanted to say have just been reading your article in the Daily Mail, made me laugh and cry at the same time, only other writer that has had that effect on me is Jane Austen. *Kathryn*

We were so sad to hear about your latest setback and can only imagine its impact upon you and your family. You have been so brave for so long and really deserve some better news soon. *Lynda and your friends in Denby Dale*

Adrian. I cannot overstate how moved and inspired I was by your appearance on 'Breakfast' yesterday. I have been wondering what the world would be like if there were more people like you in it. *Stella*

HEART BREAK

April 4, 2008

This time I have some really sad news.

Poppy has called off the wedding and decided to separate.

I have never been so sad in all my life.

I am utterly heartbroken.

But the most difficult thing is that I don't blame her.

There was no big argument; I think there was just the slow realisation of what getting married to me means.

She also has a new job up in Hartlepool and all these factors together made her think she could make a clean break.

As for me I already miss her so much and my life is in tatters.

Poppy was my best friend and soul mate.

I'd been with her for over seven years and before all this started we had shared some incredible times and been to some amazing places.

If you are reading this I want you to know how much you meant to me and that I will never forget you.

She told me that basically she didn't feel the same way about me any more.

That doesn't necessarily mean my illness is directly to blame but its changed how I look, stopped me being able to travel like we used to, stopped me becoming who I wanted to be professionally. Every day someone has to help me put creams on my back to control Graft versus Host Disease, my skin is flaking and sore.

I feel revolting.

When she said yes to my proposal I could see in her eyes that she meant it and really wanted to give it a go.

But something has changed in the last month.

Part of me feels less guilty now knowing that she is free; free from me, free from this disease and able to be exactly who she wants to be.

She is a wonderful person who has provided the most loyal support to me throughout the last year and a half.

She is about to start a new job too and I think, on some level, she thought she had a way out.

I genuinely wish her all the best and whoever she does eventually marry will be a very lucky man indeed.

As for me I have no idea what to do.

The number of cruel circumstances stacked against me just seem astonishing. I hope you agree from reading this blog I am not prone to self pity but I really do not know what I have done to deserve all this.

Poppy was the bit of hope I had built my crumbling existence on.

I promised myself that if I survived my bone marrow transplant I would propose to her. Thinking of how much fun our wedding would be was one of the main focal points I used to survive.

She also said she was happy to sign up to IVF treatment and that if I did die it would be great having a child that reminded her of me.

Just by saying that helped me more than she will ever know.

If we had split up four years ago it would have been difficult but ultimately fine. I would have enjoyed going out and being single again.

Graft versus Host Disease means I have less energy, the steroids affect parts of the body in an unpleasant way, I don't look right and as I mentioned in my previous post (before this emotional turmoil) my stomach has started to play up again.

This means I feel sick a lot of the time and my appetite has gone.

I've temporarily moved back in with my parents and they have been great.

But I'm 26 and don't know what to do next.

Before I would have happily moved into a shared house or got a flat on my own.

Unfortunately my time in isolation has fundamentally scarred me.

I can no longer bear being on my own for long periods of time. I really need company and the comfort of other human beings.

No one's going to marry me now so I somehow need to address the fact that I'm never going to have a family or children of my own.

Before anyone posts any comments along the lines of "Don't worry, it will be alright," please consider the reality of the situation.

I think I have really made the best of the hand I have been dealt but now I can genuinely see no way out.

Good points
- I have got the most loving family and friends you could wish for. They have all been so supportive.
- I have got a job I like and my colleagues at the Huddersfield Examiner have again been brilliant.

Bad points
- Can't have children.
- Leukaemia might be coming back (results will probably be OK from this week's test).
- Graft versus Host Disease is causing all sort of problems. My skin is red and sore in places, it's flaking off at the back of my neck, energy levels are poor so I can't even go out and get drunk, it might be spreading to my stomach which means even more steroids.
- My face is bloated and I look ugly. Sometimes I feel like I've been sunburnt.
- My hair is really strange.
- I can't exercise or get in shape because the steroids have weakened my legs.
- Very unlikely that I will ever get better.
- Even if I don't get a nasty infection and die my life expectancy has been slashed.
- I will need cataract surgery at some point this year.
- I will develop problems with my gums because of the radiotherapy. This also means I am prone to secondary cancers too.
- My ambition was to be a national reporter but I have not got the energy or the ability to move to London and work shifts.
- I'm stuck in a job with a modest wage so how can I ever set up home on my own?
- Need to sort out the flat and work out how we are going to divide up all the stuff.
- Don't have enough energy to up and leave and just do something completely different.

I'm lost, deeply upset and have no idea what to do.

COMMENTS (86)

Nothing I can say will make any difference, however remembering one of my favourite quotes from John Updike: "Dreams come true; without that possibility, nature would not incite us to have them". Apology for sounding a little 'don't worry it'll be alright'. *Rob*

SAVED BY MY FAMILY, MY FRIENDS AND THIS BLOG
April 18, 2008

Just over a week ago I nearly took my own life.

I had drunk a generous glass of whiskey and was lying on my bed. I am sorry to say it now but I have never felt so worthless and empty. Despite everything I have been through there just seemed no point in carrying on.

There was no hope at all.

An overdose seemed the most logical option. I had even worked out the order in which I was going to consume the copious amounts of tablets stuffed in a bag by my bedside.

I'm ashamed to write this but that is the truth and I suppose this is what my blog is all about.

To indicate just how serious I was I had started playing all my Radiohead albums! God I'm a cliché.

What stopped me in the end was maybe cowardice - a drugs overdose will be a slow and painful death - but mainly thinking about just how cruel it would have been on my family.

I know there are lots of people, including readers of this blog, who care about me and don't want me to die - even though I care much less now.

When it came to it I just couldn't do it.

This is how I turned things around with a lot of help from some wonderful people.

I should point out that I also stopped taking ALL my protective medicines.

My head has started to look more normal again. It's not better yet but it's got to the stage where if someone didn't know me they would just think I'd eaten a bit too much over Easter.

That was one thing to feel better about.

I have not cut my hair since being properly bald.

Believe it or not but in my teens I had the most magnificent mane. Some say blond curtains have gone out of fashion and that the undercut was merely an ill thought out style of the mid 90s, but I beg to differ.

Post chemotherapy my hair has returned but incredibly dark and curly. It looks like a black cauliflower has sprouted on top of my noggin.

Something I had always promised myself was that I would treat myself to my first professional haircut. Previously the most I'd spent was £3 in an establishment which sported a sign warning customers that their hair would not be cut were they to have head lice.

The hairdresser worked a minor miracle and my hair looks much like what it used to. She even got the straighteners out at one point - an experience I never thought I'd have.

During that week my editor Roy phoned up and asked if I was coming to our group's in-house awards do in Liverpool. I said I wasn't going to go and he sounded very disappointed. He seemed oddly insistent.

Anyway, after my haircut, I went back to stay with my parents and went out and got very drunk with my best friend Ben.

I know not all readers of this blog will approve of me getting drunk. However, you have to remember that I'm British and drinking heavily is one of the few things we Brits actually do well.

It really helped and made me see life with a renewed vigour.

The next day I decided to try on my suit and it fitted again. A clear sign the effects of the steroids were reversing. With that I phoned up the boss, asked for a week off and said I would be coming to the awards ceremony on Friday.

It was one of the best decisions I have ever made.

The do in Liverpool was excellent. It was held in Sefton Park in a magnificent palm house. All the tables were candle lit and set amid a dazzling array of plants and trees. There we were eating this fabulous meal beneath a star-lit sky and a few awards were given.

Then I was picked as the overall winner of the excellence awards - check out this video by Claire Gray. It's great stuff but trust her to include the dancing bits. I kind of hoped no one would ever see that again. No wonder Roy wanted me to come!

The background music is UK group the Sugababes. I can't imagine Heidi regularly sits down to read about Graft versus Host Disease but if she does please don't sue us.

After all this me and some colleagues from Liverpool, including Liam McNeilis who you may remember from the Vegas award, headed into town.

We ended up in this wicked bar and one of the best things for me was I met this girl who said I was lovely looking. In fact, she said I was "hot".

After feeling so rubbish about my appearance for so long that was one of the nicest things anyone could have said to me.

If she's reading this I just want to say thank you so much.

The following day I headed down to London where I stayed with Will, a friend from journalism college, and his girlfriend Brook. It was their housewarming party and I got to meet some really interesting people.

London people are hilarious. In general, they have no idea where anything is north of the M25.

Not only did one person, an Oxford graduate no less, not know where Huddersfield is, she also thought it's pronounced Huddlesfield.

Harold Wilson would be turning in his grave.

After that I went to stay with my mate Olie, in Balham. We had a great time. One day was crazy and booze-fuelled culminating in a particularly exciting game of Trivial Pursuit.

I had such a good time and was able to see lots of my friends and discuss a number of bone marrow donation issues with Caroline, from the Anthony Nolan Trust.

Every one of you helped me so much.

Thank you again to all my long-suffering and relentlessly loving family, Ben, Gav, Caroline, Nel, Hollie, Phil, everyone at the Huddersfield Examiner and Liverpool Echo, Will, Brook, Olie, James, Lisa, Ashley, Lucy, Caroline B, Megan, Jen and Rachel.

Lots more people have phoned and spoken to me.

And of course all of you who took the time to comment and wish me well.

This was one situation I couldn't get out of myself - I needed pulling out which you all did in different ways.

One other interesting observation is that because I'm in such a difficult situation some people realise there is not much more they can say.

As a fall back they just tell me their deepest, darkest secrets. One I still can't quite believe!

I wanted to end with a dream I had while travelling around the country.

I am on a plane that is on fire and making a crash landing.

The top of the plane has been ripped off and it's soaring over a school field with kids playing football.

Everyone else is panicking but I'm just sat there with my legs dangling in the powerful oncoming air; laughing.

COMMENTS (97)

I'm glad you're still with us! I can't imagine how you've been feeling. You sound as if you've come through the worst... I know it's not all better by any means but your family and friends must have given you a reason to live and perhaps let some light in? I hope that makes sense. Oh, and step away from the Radiohead albums!!! *Catherine*

You didn't take your life BECAUSE you thought of everyone else and not yourself which is what YOU do so thank you for that! *Lucy*

Just wanted to say hello and tell you that we're all thinking of you and love you lots. *Hels & all your P3 posse p.s. That girl was right you are damn hot.*

THE DRUGS DON'T WORK...
May 1, 2008

How many times can someone get kicked in the head and keep picking themselves up?

This latest blow has well and truly floored me. I've tried my best to turn this situation around, carry on with work, and see my friends, but I just can't do it.

Now before I drown you all with my unrelenting misery I'd like to say thank you to all the new readers and the people who have taken the time to comment.

As you can see from previous posts I really think it's important that I should reply to people who have given their time to support me and wish me well.

This time I have been unable to keep up with the huge numbers of people dropping me a line. I apologise for that.

But I would like to say that despite everything that's happened to me those comments did help and provided a much needed lift from the gloom.

For all of you who are following this blog outside the UK my story was featured in one of our national newspapers the Daily Mail this week. The Mail has a huge circulation, well over two million copies sold a day, and I would say one of its main focuses is health.

As you can see the response from that piece has been quite incredible so to all the new readers welcome on board.

However, the upbeat stuff ends here - this is not a particularly fun post. I also apologise for that.

Since the separation I have really felt like I no longer have anything to live for. As I explained before ALL my hope was resting on that wedding and having a family.

The trip to see my friends was great but that had to end. I had to come back to real life.

As I have said to my medical team - on many occasions - if they could fix any of the following I know I would be OK;

- Dry and itchy skin.
- Infertility.

- Restore my energy levels. I am always a bit tired and can only manage brief walks.
- Enable my body to play any of the sports I used to love so much.
- Give me back a full life expectancy.
- Immune system.
- Let me go on hot and sunny holidays abroad (the skin will react badly to intense UV light).

I'd love to get away and travel like I used to but it's just so much harder now.

I'm so tired of going through the same routine every day. Get up, do work, go in the shower, moisturise, wash with special emollient shower gel, use special shampoos, wash with steroid lotions, come out, dry off, apply moisturiser over all the body, have to use a special back applicator now I'm on my own, then put on a layer of steroid cream too. After that you put your clothes on and it always feels the same - cold and gloopy.

Every day the Graft versus Host Disease throws up new problems.

My steroids were down to 2.5mg a day (the next drop in the dose would have been to come off them altogether) but then my eyebrows and eyelashes started to come out. This is because my rogue immune system is attacking these hair follicles. Not my chest, back or shoulders. Oh no, it's the hair that everyone will really notice.

Every day eyelashes would scrape my eyeball and be incredibly irritating.

To combat this I took the steroid dose back up to 5mg and I've managed to save them for the time being.

I'm just utterly fed up with the situation I'm in and am helpless to escape from.

Anyway, something has happened, maybe my brain has imploded, but since the separation I have chosen not to take any of my pills; with the exceptions of those keeping my skin under control.

These pills include my artificial immune system. Antibiotics, antivirals and anti fungals. I am at a very high risk of a very unpleasant, potentially fatal infection.

More worryingly I have also stopped taking a drug called Glivec. This is an incredible medicine that should be keeping my chronic leukaemia at bay. If you recall the last sample showed it had returned slightly. I have no idea what damage I have done to myself here.

I am still waiting for the results of the recent bone marrow test. The following one could be more interesting.

You might find this behaviour unacceptable and I have to confess I am really ashamed of myself after everything I've been through.

I just can't alter my frame of mind.

To me this seems like the only rational choice.

I confessed all this to my excellent team and they were understandably concerned.

The next step on this journey was to see a clinical psychiatrist for depression.

I have never had any problems with my mental health and I still argue that I'm not clinically depressed.

What human being wouldn't be a bit miffed with all the shite that has been hurled at me?

However, I did take her advice and started a course of anti-depressants.

She prescribed Citalopram but I reacted to it very badly.

For a week I was sleeping 12 hours a day and waking up with what I can only describe as a terrible hangover. I was groggy, drowsy and felt awful.

That medication was stopped and yesterday she prescribed another one from the same family of drugs called Fluoxetine aka Prozac.

Happy days.

I'm in a right mess and for the first time in my life have no idea what to do.

COMMENTS (86)

Please don't do anything that could jeopardise your chance of future happiness, albeit a different kind to the one you imagined and wanted. No one can say how they would feel given the same situation, but you have managed to win the hearts of so many people in writing your blog and you wouldn't want to let us down would you? *Carol*

I read your story in the Daily Mail last night and started reading your blog from the very beginning this morning. I work as a nurse in the city hospital in Belfast and I have never read anything like it, or come across someone who faces illness, and everything that goes with it, with such courage. Please don't give up. The world needs more people like you. *Suzanne*

BONE MARROW RESULTS
May 9, 2008

I thought nothing could shock me after everything I have been through in the last 18 months.

Then I finally got the news today from my most recent bone marrow sample.

Please bear in mind this test was carried out before I went mental and stopped taking my pills.

At that stage I was taking the drug Glivec which should be effective against the chronic/strange form of the disease.

But, as regular readers will know from my weekly whinges, I have also had that post transplant complication known as Graft versus Host Disease.

Collectively, these bad boys should have stopped any leukaemia from returning.

Well today was a bit of a shocker to say the least.

Not only have we been unsuccessful at forcing the chronic condition into retreat but it has also got worse.

The cells at a molecular level are showing multiple and complex genetic abnormalities.

The bone marrow transplant has effectively failed.

I could see from my medical team that they were really surprised by the results too.

This weird chronic, proliferative disorder, has been the bane of my treatment from the start. It was the reason why chemotherapy failed and I had to have a transplant.

It's survived tons of chemotherapy, radiotherapy and a new immune system intent on hunting it out.

It's like the Chuck Norris of cancers.

If these results had been from a sample taken later I would have blamed myself for not taking the drugs and for allowing my mind to be defeated.

But this had nothing to do with it. The results are from a sample taken five weeks ago.

For new readers to this blog I sometimes wonder if you think I am making this shite up. My life has gone crazy and seems to derail spectacularly every seven to 12 days.

I wish I was making all this up. I promise you, up until I was 25 I had a fairly steady existence which included a girlfriend, going to work, going out and playing football once a week with colleagues.

Now I'm like a character in Hollyoaks, just slightly less attractive.

The plan now is I have to go back into hospital on Monday for an 'emergency' bone marrow sample.

The doctors will look at that and ask:

Can we see the leukaemia in the bone marrow cells under a microscope?
If the answer is yes, then it means there has been a major relapse of the disease and the only likely option would be more chemotherapy.

If the answer is no, there has only been a slight, molecular relapse, then the next question would be:

Are these cancerous cells responsive to Glivec?
If the answer to that is yes then I will continue to take a higher dose. I started taking it again today and promptly vomited.

If the answer is no then doctors will consult with research teams to find out if there are any available treatments that may help me.

If there are not then chemotherapy again would be a possibility.

Things may change but at this stage I am very reluctant to go down a route involving any more intensive therapy.

We are reaching the stage where we have to honestly ask ourselves would something like chemotherapy actually help or just delay the inevitable.

If it is really bad news then we are looking at weeks to months rather than years.

There are many difficult questions that could lie ahead but until we get the results back from Monday - probably by Wednesday - it's not worth dwelling on them.

I'm off tomorrow to London on another mini road trip.

Will post an update early next week.

Many thanks again for all the kind comments. I read them all and they do help me a lot.

COMMENTS (46)

You are one helluva man going through a terrible time - although not alone. There are many folk reading your amazing story who, like me, feel awful for you and helpless to help you. We can reach out with cyber hugs and kisses and all the good hopes that once again you will have a reprieve from this darn awful cancer. *Kate*

DO NOT BE DISHEARTENED. If your medical team realise that Glivec is not working there are many other drugs available. We have many patients at Addenbrooke's Cambridge where Glivec does not work but other similar drugs put them into a full remission. So have faith! *Paul*

I live in Huddersfield and have been following your story ever since I read about your diagnosis in the Examiner. Like everyone else, I can't really find the 'right' words to say because I don't think there are any 'right words', are there? The best I can come up with, is to say thank you for writing such provocative, powerful and inspirational words. In this celeb obsessed world of ours, it really is inspirational to read about real people with real lives who rise to the challenge of dealing with what life throws at them with all the gusto they can manage. *Ruth*

THANKS FOR THE WEEKEND
May 12, 2008

And so begins a potentially difficult week.

In a few hours I will have a crucial bone marrow sample taken.

The results, which we are hoping to learn on Wednesday or Thursday, will show one of two things.

- This relapse can be controlled by drugs.
- I will have to choose whether to have further intensive treatment or not.

Not a particularly pleasant set of circumstances but on the plus side I did have an excellent weekend.

I'm hoping today that the doctors don't ask me how many units of alcohol I've consumed because I will clearly have to lie.

On Saturday my friend Ben and I cruised down to London in my hot new wheels - or the Vauxhall Vectra as some people prefer to call it.

He went off to see his family and I went to hang out with an old journalist college friend called Laura, in St Albans.

We went out for lunch, and a few drinks, and I confessed that I had no real plans. She was great though. She offered to put me up and said I could come out with her mates around town later.

I don't know if you can do 'shout-outs' in blogs but if you can, here's one to everyone I had the pleasure of meeting on Saturday.

Thanks for such a fun time.

I met some lovely people and they really helped take my mind off everything.

Anyway, after many more drinks, games of cards (yes, it was that sort of random night) we ended up in some club which seemed to be in the middle of nowhere.

The music was excellent but by that time I was so out of it I was unable to bust those special dance moves I have treated all of you to before.

That was probably a good thing.

I think we left about 3am and I seem to remember being in a cab full of really cool girls all singing: "We love you taxi" to the tune of I Can't Take My Eyes Off You.

Needless to say I was a little delicate the next day.

My grandma in Nottingham has been excellent throughout all this.

She has come up with lots of little ideas for treats that include things like theatre tickets and dinner at the House of Lords.

Big Grandma has quite an impressive social network!

One of her ideas was to treat me and friends to lunch at Gordon Ramsey's restaurant, The Maze, near Mayfair, in London.

She arranged for some money to be left behind the bar and for us to treat ourselves to some really good food.

The plan was that me Ben and my friend Olie would all meet there at 12.30pm.

Ben was quite fresh but I was struggling.

However, Olie was in a terrible state.

Me and Ben arrived first and sat down with a glass of sparkling mineral water.

Then Olie rocked up, strides through this beautiful restaurant, clutching a Boots carrier bag.

Joining us he sits down at our posh table, opens his carrier bag and takes out a bottle of water fizzing with Alka Selza!

We must have looked a right sight.

The food was delicious though. I tried smoked eels, quail eggs, sea trout and a beautiful rhubarb crumble.

It was a lovely treat and we were looked after incredibly well by the staff – boy did we need it.

So thanks again Grandma.

Now the fun temporarily stops but whatever the outcome I hope I have the ability to handle the results with dignity and courage.

COMMENTS (44)

I'm glad that you had such a great weekend! And dignity and courage is all that you've shown here so far- you'll handle whatever is coming. *Jen*

THE BEGINNING OF THE END
May 14, 2008

In the rapping words of Craig David: "RE-EE-Lapse".

After everything we have been through together I am so sorry to break the following news to you all.

The leukaemia has reappeared in the bone marrow and I have only got weeks or months to live.

In the end I decided to have no further intensive treatment.

I had made up my mind a long time ago that if I was given this news I would stay healthy for as long as possible and enjoy spending time with my friends and family.

This might sound strange to some of you but after talking to my medical team today I am still confident I have made the right choice - the fact that it was my choice was also important.

I could have contracted an infection and died in circumstances beyond my control.

The facts of the matter were this strange, chronic version of the disease, has already resisted the following;

- Two cycles of chemotherapy.
- High dose chemotherapy and radiotherapy before the bone marrow transplant.
- A new immune system from my donated cells which was supposed to hunt it out.
- The drug Glivec which has transformed the treatment of classic chronic myeloid leukaemia.

My consultant said the chance of more chemotherapy leading to a long-term cure was perhaps around 20%.

If there were no side effects, and I could have had it over a couple of hours then gone home, I might have considered it.

As anyone who has undergone chemo for leukaemia will tell you it's horrible.

But more importantly, as it wipes out the bone marrow cells which create your immune system, you can't leave the ward until it has regenerated sufficiently. This can take up to three weeks.

Put simply, I've had enough.

I have thought if maybe I was older, Poppy and I had married and we had children, then maybe my thought process would be different.

As it stands my quality of life has been greatly reduced by my Graft versus Host Disease (GvHD) and I have never quite recovered from the bone marrow transplant.

My mind still wants to do all the things any 26-year-old can do - but I can't.

I am thinking a lot at the moment about my wonderful parents, sister Carrie and the rest of my family. Their support and loyalty throughout everything warranted a thoroughly better outcome.

They don't deserve any of this.

As for me I'm feeling OK. I've been preparing for this eventuality now for the best part of 18 months.

I've led a decent life, seen a lot of the world and been in a job I've enjoyed.

As for dying - how can anyone be scared of something that is going to happen to every single one of us?

The crux of the matter is that in the next couple of weeks I will become progressively ill as my bone marrow cells get increasingly out of control.

The most likely cause of death will be a nasty infection.

One of the saddest aspects for me is that I hoped Baldy's Blog would shine out as a beacon in the too often tragic world of blood cancers.

I honestly thought I had conquered the leukaemia, that I could manage the GvHD, get married and have children.

I really wanted that to be the end of this story and show that people can overcome this disease.

Well the message I want readers to take is that people regularly do. There are so many success stories for every person this doesn't work out for.

I have been EXCEPTIONALLY unlucky.

Anyway, there are a few more things I want to take care of so you've not heard the last of me yet.

Thank you again for every single word you have all posted. I've had some terrible times over the last year and a half and you have no idea just what comfort they have provided.

COMMENTS (455)

I think you're one of the bravest people I've ever heard of. God Bless you. You will be in my thoughts and prayers always. *Jim*

You are a remarkably strong individual and I so wish that there was some treatment to help you. Thinking of you and your family and I don't know what else to say. *Susan*

I saw your feature on TV tonight. I am O Rhesus negative if I can be any good to you I would walk barefoot on broken glass to donate for you. I have been through a lot of personal stuff these last few years but feel ashamed of how I have dealt with it when I think of your strength. *Mark*

Your blog did reach it's goal for being a shining hope for others. Living whatever time we have is the point of life. You have shown us that. *Baldylocks*

A PLEA FOR MORE BONE MARROW DONORS
May 15, 2008

I have one last little mission before I die.

I'm determined to try and educate more people about what it is like to be a bone marrow donor.

There are still 7,000 people - children and adults in the UK alone - who are waiting to find a match.

Without your help they have no hope.

At least I was given a chance.

The problem is people think it is some horrific procedure and I want to show as many people as possible that it is not like that.

Apparently, the Germans have one of the world's best marrow registers. All they do is educate their sixth form students about why it's important to donate blood, bone marrow and how you do it.

Why can't we do that here?

If you want to get on one of the donor registers all you have to do is ask about it next time you give blood.

The National Blood Service provides a bone marrow register.

Alternatively, you could get in touch with the Anthony Nolan Trust.

They can send out a special blood testing kit which you can take with you to your GP.

You then post your sample back to the trust.

Specialists can tell from your blood whether you are a potential tissue match for someone or not. Your details are then entered onto one of the databases.

The two organisations work together so you only need to be on one.

If you were a match for someone who needed a transplant, and you still wanted to help, you would be given a number of injections of a naturally occurring hormone called Granulocyte Colony Stimulating Factor (G-CSF), four days prior to the donation.

This stimulates your bone marrow to increase blood cell production. For example, when you are ill, GCSF stimulates the marrow to make more white blood cells to fight off infection.

The injections are safe and the only side effect I experienced when I was given some on the ward was a slight ache in my bones.

A donor is then brought into hospital and hooked up to a machine called a cell separator.

As you can see from the above video a needle is put in one arm and the blood goes into the machine. The stem cells are separated by centrifugation and flow into a bag. The other parts of the blood are then returned back to the donor through a different needle.

The whole process takes around four hours.

Current research shows that these types of stem cells are the best for curing leukaemia.

However, for some conditions such as aplastic anaemia, stem cells direct from the bone marrow are more desirable.

To get these cells a bone marrow harvest is performed. This can require a two-night stay in hospital.

When I have a bone marrow sample I have to lie on my side in the foetal position. I am given a local anaesthetic and a needle is inserted into the bony bits at the back of my pelvis.

A donor is given a general anaesthetic and the same procedure is carried out but at multiple sites.

There is no bone-breaking or spine jeopardising - that is not to say it wouldn't be a bit sore in the morning!

None of these procedures are anything to be taken lightly and do represent a big commitment.

The databases are expensive to maintain so they only want people on there who are determined to help.

Donors have the final say about which method they prefer.

Ideally, it is best to be OK with both. That way if someone is unable to extract enough bone marrow cells, another option for the recipient is possible.

On a personal note I used to give blood but I never joined a bone marrow register because I thought the procedure could leave you paralysed.

That, as I hope you can see, could not be further from the truth.

I'd just like to add that we live in a world that for all its good is riddled with problems and selfishness.

Joining a register is one of the true acts of altruism and human kindness.

Who knows, you may end up saving someone else on the other side of the planet.

COMMENTS (421)

I have lost count of how many times I have written and then deleted a response following the awful news of your relapse. Words simply cannot express how sad I am that it has come to this. You are the most extraordinarily persuasive and compelling young man who will go on being an inspiration to others all over the world. Following this most recent entry I will say that it will be my absolute pleasure to become a bone marrow donor and I am only sorry that I have not done it before now. *Elaine, New York*

> In a shitty selfish world, you have become so important as a beacon of what people can be like at their very best. *Denise*

WHEN ADRIAN MET GORDON
May 22, 2008

Adrian met Prime Minister Gordon Brown to discuss his leukaemia campaign. It was high profile and made most of the national TV news channels.

COMMENTS (34)

Saw your story on msnbc.com and I am sorry that your cancer has returned. I live in the U.S. and I have been inspired by your story. If your mission is to have more people, no matter where they live, to sign up to donate then your goal is one step closer. I am now actively looking for a place to donate. *Kevin, USA*

Thank you for sharing your experience. I have found it truly humbling. After reading through all of your posts, I thought that the best way to honor you was to share how easy it is to become a donor with my friends and family. Like many, I give blood and have never thought about being a bone marrow donor. Your story has inspired me to get on the registry here. *Dustina, USA*

I came across your blog today and am truly amazed at the strength and courage you have to battle what you are going through - plus keep us readers informed of the needs and importance of the donations we can make to help make a difference. I live in a very small town in Wyoming, USA (400 people). I think it has made us forget how lucky we are and how important is is to help those in need. I am glad you have lots of friends and family to support you - sometimes just having someone to talk to is one of the best things that there is. Be strong... Keep positive and remember you always have ones who love you. *Jan, USA*

You are a beautiful person from what I can tell from the inside out. You are still quite a handsome man and a hottie. *Donna, USA*

BALDY'S BACK
May 24, 2008

I think it's fair to say that went pretty well.

Videos about blood, bone marrow and organ donation.

I firmly believe that if our young adults are given all the facts about these important issues many more will go on to become donors themselves.

Backed by the Huddersfield Examiner and local MP Kali Mountford I honestly believe this can happen.

While I was in London the Anthony Nolan Trust told me the numbers waiting for bone marrow transplants had actually increased.

They are currently trying to find matches for 16,000 requests, mainly from the UK, but also for patients around the world.

Without matches these people will die.

As well as meeting Prime Minister Gordon Brown to discuss this idea, I was also able to chat with the Health Secretary Alan Johnson and Education Secretary Ed Balls.

Just to say a big thank you to Kali. Her desire to help and to actually arrange these meetings was incredible and I am hugely grateful for all her considerable efforts.

This then is the story of a crazy couple of days and me being an outrageous media whore.

I drove down to London on Saturday in preparation for a busy week ahead. I had always planned to do this, no matter what the outcome of my treatment had been - good or bad.

In the UK there is a huge problem with the perception of bone marrow donation. No one seems to know much about it at all.

I enjoyed the FA Cup final with some beers and some dirty take away food. Forget smoked eels at Gordon Ramsey's - sometimes kebab meat and chips are just what you need.

Sunday and Monday were taken up with organisation calls and emails.

It was on Tuesday that things really started to kick off.

Much of the morning was spent in north London filming pre-recorded bits for BBC Breakfast.

It was the phone that was the problem - it never stopped ringing.

I'd answer one call then have voicemails waiting once I'd finished. I'd listen to them then a further six had come in while I was listening to the first lot.

At one point my friend Caroline, from the Anthony Nolan Trust, helped me out while I was filming. Apparently one researcher asked her if she was my PA!

I got in a taxi to do some filming with the Yorkshire TV news then I decided I wanted to make a bit more of an effort.

I flagged down another cab and asked the driver to take me to the nearest suit shop. I decided that if I was going out in the House of Commons, and meeting all these important people, I should really try and look the part.

They were great and even ironed my shirt.

I just wore the whole ensemble out of the shop. That's the kind of behaviour people who are dying should indulge in more often.

On the way into the Commons I met Alan Johnson - Secretary of State for Health. He listened and was quite knowledgeable of the subject because one of his constituents had been involved in a hunt for a bone marrow match.

He was very supportive and really seemed keen to help out as much as he could. He said there was already a pilot scheme for 14 and 15-year-olds so I said let's expand this to the key age of 17/18 where you are old enough to join the register if you so choose.

Mr Johnson also said he would look into whether there was money available to help raise awareness, possibly in the form of some national campaign.

I was then able to meet Education Secretary, Ed Balls. He was really helpful. He explained that the Citizenship scheme - which I didn't realise ran through secondary education into college - would provide a structure on which to hang this talk off.

With business concluded, Kali then treated me and Caroline, along with her husband Ian, to a superb meal in a splendid restaurant in the Commons.

The food was exceptionally good and the pudding trolley was worth the trip in itself!

The meeting with Gordon Brown on Wednesday was a great experience.

In the UK Mr Brown is criticised for not being as relaxed in the media as Tony Blair was, but one to one he is really approachable, good company and listened to everything I had to say.

I am still quite touched that he spent a good 20 minutes of his time with me – that is a hell of a lot of time for this issue when you have got a country to run.

Later that day it was reported he was meeting with other OPEC leaders to discuss ways of reducing world oil prices and yet there he was chatting to this guy from Sheffield with a suit and daft hat on.

What I've always liked about this campaign is that it's easy to sort out and would not cost much money.

Mr Brown even suggested taking it a step further and seeing if we could get a video campaign to support it.

He asked me to suggest a couple of celebrities I thought would be good to front it and that he would personally write to them on my behalf.

Don't get me wrong, Mr Brown is a skilled politician with a towering intellect. Nothing was committed to during that chat.

But I left the meeting feeling like he really wanted to help and that some sort of lasting change is going to take place.

Adrian Sudbury: Media Tart

Just for the record I thought you might like an idea of what it was like for me on Wednesday. It did go pretty mental.

1. 6.30am. Wake up in Regent's Park Hotel. Breakfast show arranged car over to BBC studio.
2. Car doesn't turn up so have to jump in cab.
3. End up in green room getting nose powdered.
4. Into studio, meet presenters Bill and Susanna. Always had a little bit of a thing for Susanna so glad she was nice in real life. She asked me if I liked Genesis because they were on next. I said no and we laughed.
5. Interview went well then popped upstairs to take part in Victoria Derbyshire's show on 5Live.
6. Great to meet her and all her team who I have spoken so much to on the phone.
7. Arrange to meet local TV and Channel 5 news at Westminster at 11.30.
8. Feedback from listeners really good. Lots of support for the idea and people sending in tons of good comments.
9. Quick change into suit then jump in a car (the media outlets arrange all these for you).
10. Ten missed calls, five voicemails, 11 texts.
11. Use the car time to try and get through them all but becoming increasingly difficult.
12. Shoot pre-pieces outside Westminster with Channel 5 news and local ITV news.
13. 12.50pm, meet Kali Mountford MP and her office manager at St Stephen's entrance.

14. Confusion over who is allowed into film. End up with three crews, the MP and me all traipsing through security. Real media circus.
15. People beginning to recognise me and shake my hand in the street. Incredible feeling. All supportive and saying what a good idea it is.
16. Arrive outside meeting room in House of Commons. Final say from Downing Street Press Office. It's a private meeting but there will be an opportunity at the end to get some film/stills.
17. Complete meeting and dash over to Westminster studios to do a live piece with ITN lunch time news.
18. Back out into the parks around Parliament to finish filming with local ITV news and Channel 5.
19. Free half hour so grab lunch in the Commons with Kali and Ian. Pasty, a pie, brown sauce and a lager shandy.
20. Back out into Parliament Square to record a piece for the local BBC news.
21. Another car back to the national BBC news centre to appear on BBC news 24 channel.
22. Cup of tea, quick change back into normal clothes, a few biscuits, and charge phone back up.
23. Interview goes out live at 5.30pm then off in another car to NBC studios.
24. Record more of a magazine piece with them then get another car back to Balham for a glass of red bull and a packet of crisps!
25. Get to my car and drive home.
26. Arrive back at parents near Nottingham just before midnight. Mum lovingly prepares some spaghetti and a glass of red wine.

That was quite a day!

I have to add for the record that I am not brave.

Loads of people - especially on TV - keep saying that to me.

I'm not dodging bullets in Afghanistan, losing my child, challenging difficult children or keeping our streets safe.

All I've ever done is get ill and write about it.

That said all these wonderful comments are overwhelming, fantastic to read and often breathtaking. I've had to set my mum on as a full time moderator! I think she quite likes doing it though.

One final point.

When I got back to Sheffield it turned out my blood counts had really dropped. I had done all this with the equivalent of three bags of blood missing from my body.

That is hardcore.

COMMENTS (48)

You've accomplished a lot, and three pints low, I am in awe. Your ambition to educate the rest of us has inspired me. *Natalie*

Certainly is hardcore! Pleased to say that due to your campaign I started the ball rolling enrolling myself for bone marrow donation, and I think I might bully some mates into doing the same thing. *Lisa*

Thank you so much for writing this blog. I don't think I've ever been so touched by something written by a complete stranger. Your positive attitude is so inspiring, and I'm convinced your campaign will succeed beyond all expectations. *Anna*

Thank you...you have given me the slap in the face I needed!! I've been moping around feeling sorry for myself for the last few months as a single, working parent struggling to pay the bills! You've given me a reason to lay off the vodka. *Chelle*

BACK OUR CAMPAIGN

May 25, 2008

All I am trying to achieve is the following:

A 40 minute talk to all second year sixth form students about why it is important to think about donating blood, bone marrow and organs.

If you think this is a good idea please sign the Downing Street Petition which is available to be signed by all UK residents.

I think a healthy discussion about all these issues, where our young adults are given all the facts and are able to engage in a debate, will be of benefit to many.

I don't believe anyone should be forced to do anything they feel uncomfortable with.

But it's only right that people should be able to make an informed choice either way.

At the moment there is too much misconception surrounding these procedures.

There is also an urgent need for blood, bone marrow and organ donors to come forward.

If people donate blood, or join a bone marrow register in their teens, then they will often continue to give blood and they will be on the register for a long time.

These databases are expensive to maintain so it's important that as many young and committed people are involved.

Imagine if these talks do go ahead and maybe only 10% of all the students decide to sign up to either the Blood Service or the Anthony Nolan bone marrow register. (Remember, they work together so you only need to be on one).

That's an incredible amount of young people coming onto the register every year. The same would apply to blood donation too.

Now the plan is to try and get as many people to back our campaign as possible.

After the recess the Huddersfield MPs will return to Parliament and raise the issue again.

This will be in the form of tabling a motion or highlighting it with a Prime Minister's Question.

Thank you for your help.

I'd just like to add that all the comments have been superb.

For those who have just discovered the blog it has turned into quite a tale hasn't it?

For those who have been with me since the beginning - Liz, Annie, Claire, Dawn, and all the rest, what a carry on!

Best wishes to you all. x

COMMENT (99)

My 16-year-old will be going into sixth form in September and he says he wants to bring up the donation debate in citizenship. As a mother of a beautiful healthy boy I can't imagine what your parents must be going through, however I think they will be eternally proud of your dignity, fight, ambition, humour and obvious care you show for your fellow human beings. *Lesley*

SUDDERS DOES AL JAZEERA
May 28, 2008

"Adrian, we heard about your story and wondered if we could get you on the show to talk about the campaign."
-Sure, no problem. When were you thinking?
"Monday, 8pm, we will arrange a car to take you to a studio in Leeds."
-Sounds good. Out of interest where will this show be aired?
"We go out live across North America, Western Europe, much of the Middle East and South East Asia. At that time slot we tend to get viewing figures of around 140 million, but we think it's closer to 170 million."
-OK...

COMMENTS (54)

Wow up to 170 million people. Guess that must be difficult to comprehend. Well done and keep up the good work. *Amanda*

Bravo, Adrian! *Lacey*

This is amazing! The work that you are doing is going to save thousands of lives, I'm in awe! *Kim*

I saw Adrian on Al Jazeera hosted by Riz Khan. It was so moving and great, I think he should be proud of himself being that strong and trying to turn his bad experience into something good for the world by concentrating on the importance of donors. *Shaima*

BLAZE OF GLORY
June 2, 2008

I can't beat this leukaemia but I can make a difference, I'm making the most of every breath I have left, I am spending time with some of the most wonderful friends and family anyone could ask to share their lives with; but more importantly I'm going down in style.

I wish I had never been hit with this disease and I wish I could have been cured.

Neither now apply, so all I can do is keep laughing, campaigning and say: "F*ck you cancer."

How many people in their lives ever have a week like that?

I got to have dinner in the Commons, drink with Secretaries of State and then talk with the Prime Minister for 20 minutes.

I was wearing a suit and a bloody beanie hat in Parliament.

Not only that, I spoke live to millions of people on local, national and then international news. How many human beings ever get the opportunity to talk in front of up to 170 million people?

The numbers are literally head imploding if you think about it too much.

These are undoubtedly dreadful circumstances but actually it's important for me that you all know I am having a blast and making, again, the best I can of a challenging situation.

With the petition going incredibly well I am determined to leave behind a lasting change that will benefit hundreds if not thousands of people in the future.

And I think the Government are listening as well. Gordon Brown has already written back to me asking for a list of celebrities that he could write to on my behalf to be involved with a video campaign to dispel the myths of bone marrow donation.

On top of that MP Kali Mountford has said she will continue to raise our campaign in Parliament and with all your help, and that of my journalist friends, I really think the pressure can be sufficiently maintained.

I won't let this lie because I know there are so many people who are reading this blog who are waiting for, or know someone close to them, who need a transplant.

These people deserve a chance and it will be one that can be given them through better educating our young adults.

The media interest will fade now.

That was why it was important I squeezed all the awareness I could while I was flavour of the day and had good energy levels.

As we print hacks say: "Today's news, tomorrow's chip paper."

With the campaign in full swing, my energy levels are now starting to taper off but I'm not done yet.

Now is the time to spend time with those who I care about and have supported me throughout all this.

There was one other mission I needed to take care of and that was to honour my commitment to Phil Driver.

You may remember my excellent friend Phil - great guy - who ran the London Marathon on my behalf and organised a huge football tournament, all in aid of the Anthony Nolan Trust.

A couple of months ago he asked me to be his best man. I naturally agreed but had a bad feeling I might be unavailable for selection next summer.

So what I've decided to do, with help from colleagues, is make a special video speech from Liverpool - where we met at university.

The filming for that is done now and I hope it's something both he and his beautiful bride-to-be Emma really like.

House Party

None of us choose when we are going to die but it is something that will happen to us all.

So let me ask you this.

What would you do if you were in my position?

My answer is forget all that sky diving, driving a super car really fast drivel. Get your friends round, get your family round, get Johnny the German Shepherd puppy and your six-year-old cousin over, sit out in the garden, have some great food and crack open the booze.

Saturday will go down in my mind, and I'm sure many of the people who rocked up, as one of the best parties ever.

It was absolutely brilliant.

Kicking off at 1pm at my parents' house with my grandma, and friends of the family, there was then a steady squad rotation of additional family members, former Nottingham college friends, mates from journalism school, friends of friends and of course the whole crew from Liverpool University.

There were no plans as such and people just brought along a bit to drink.

My best mate Ben sorted out a lot of the food along with my wonderful Auntie Helen who also kept things ticking over behind the scenes.

My mum slow cooked a huge piece of pork so there was plenty of food for people to tuck into throughout the day.

My mum and dad have worked hard over the years to make this beautiful garden and we got so lucky with the weather.

I was keen to point out that some clown would get drunk and end up falling in the pond - but I have to say it was a very civilised affair.

Despite there being a hint of sadness this was not a mawkish gathering just one awash with laughter and old friends having a splendid time together.

Every corner you turned you could bump into another interesting conversation, another laugh about old times and people who I care so dearly about.

I loved it because although I was the reason for the party, I was not the centre of attention and I didn't feel like that's why people were there. There were no speeches or anything serious, just lots of fun.

We sat outside until close to midnight, drinking punch, wine, joking, laughing, chatting, listening to music. I honestly could not have asked for a better evening with my friends.

We then retreated indoors to this karaoke game on the Playstation called Singstar.

You have got to love that game. I love the feeling of waking up in the morning and wondering if you've got a throat infection then suddenly realising no, you were just singing badly and loudly.

Time melted into the night and I took it upon myself to look outside and make sure everything was locked up.

I got outside, lost my bearings and suddenly realised my lower legs were drenched.

I was the drunken idiot who had ended up in the pond!

Laughing, I hauled myself out and began my shameful return to the house. I took off my soaked shoes, and in true comedy fashion poured the water out of them.

I then realised I did not have another pair of trousers.

I went upstairs to try and solve this problem when I met one of my friends Nel.

We were having a laugh about the story and she was helping me come up with some spare trouser ideas when she suddenly stopped, her jaw dropped, and said: "Boy, you are bleeding!"

I looked down and saw there was a whole trail of blood throughout the house, all over my mum's wooden floors, and then this big pool on the carpet upstairs.

Well, we couldn't stop laughing.

I took off my jeans to reveal a major gash in my right shin no doubt riddled with pond bacteria and other nasties.

Thankfully, I had a bag of platelets two days before so I was pretty confident I wasn't going to bleed to death.

It was just one of those beautiful drunken moments where you are not in any pain, trying to stem a major bleed with scrunched up bits of tissue, all in a pair of unfortunately coloured bright blue boxer shorts.

Anyway, to cut a long story short one of my friends, Sarah Brown, is a newly qualified doctor and I was surrounded with health professionals who were on hand to help out.

We washed it out and patched it up - no septicaemia yet my friends - and carried on drinking.

Got to bed about 4.30am.

Just to summarise how good the party was, here is a list of things that were left behind the following day;

- A cardigan
- Two iPods
- Jewellery
- A small bit of sick close to the herbaceous border
- One sock
- A pair of girls' knickers

If anyone knows who these belong to please get in touch.

When the option was put to me about further intensive treatment; that it was unlikely to work and that potentially it could kill me - there was no choice to make.

This is how I want my friends to remember me.

Not crunched up vomiting into a sick bowl, miserable through the discomfort of chemotherapy.

But as someone standing on their feet, fighting to make a small but important difference, and most of all laughing with those I love and with those who love me.

COMMENTS (133)

Good on you Adrian! I would like to think I'd do the same. You can be confident your campaign has made a difference and will continue to do so. *Charlotte*

Way to go there drunkie, falling into the pond! Stay healthy and humoured. *Kim, Cincinnati, Ohio USA*

I have this amazing picture in my head of you. Someone very strong, much loved and someone who will be so missed by your amazing family and friends. I unfortunately now also have a picture of you with your trousers around your ankles! *With love and great admiration, Gaynor*

FIGHTING, CAMPAIGNING AND PARTYING
June 6, 2008
I am absolutely exhausted but it's worth it!

The campaign is going well and thousands of people have signed our petition - please keep signing if you haven't already and spread the word far and wide.

Kali Mountford MP phoned yesterday and said the plan is now to raise the matter in Parliament again this week, hopefully at Prime Minister's Question Time on Wednesday.

As a collective group the Huddersfield MPs are then looking at tabling a number of motions to keep the campaign on the Parliamentary agenda.

After recovering from the house party on Sunday I went to stay with a friend on Monday then headed back to Huddersfield to see all my colleagues.

I'm not quite sure how I'm doing all this but essentially I'm powered by a combination of steroids - I've increased my dose back up to 50mg a day - and knocking back cans of Red Bull energy drink.

Seems to be doing the trick.

My chest is becoming increasingly difficult but I am determined to have as much fun as possible while I still can.

The turn out on Tuesday was brilliant and really touching. Loads of people came out for a drink and it was great catching up with people I've not seen for ages.

They are a brilliant crowd and it's been a privilege working with them all.

Even the lads I used to play 5-a-side football with were there - but that was mainly to remind me how crap I was.

Having been away from the office for quite a while it was so touching to go back in and see all these posters up everywhere screaming "Sign up for Sudders!" then a picture of my big head. It was like something out of Citizen Kane.

It just showed me how much work the editorial team - and in particular reporter Katie Campling - had done behind the scenes to make all this come together.

There are two indications of just how big this campaign is becoming.

Firstly the Anthony Nolan Trust phoned the other day to tell me a THIRD of all their website traffic was now coming from this blog.

Secondly, the number of people who have signed our petition is comparable to the campaign to get Bruce Forsyth a knighthood.

This, my friends, is the big time.

Anyway, back to Tuesday.

After catching up with everyone in the office we headed down the street to bar 1535 for drinks.

There was a lovely range of ages and different people who I have worked with over the years.

People couldn't stop buying me drinks and were coming up to me and having heart to hearts. It was wonderful.

On this subject, my situation does generate some incredible responses from individuals.

I wrote in a previous post when I was so miserable that once some friends truly understood the situation all they could offer is their deepest, darkest secrets.

Although I have been incredibly unlucky and this is a tragic situation, I have equally never experienced such an outpouring of love and affection from so many.

I suppose this is something that most people will never get to experience but I have to say it is something uniquely special.

It is an opportunity many of us will not be able to have.

It's like people realise they might not see me again and just open their hearts, revealing a level of honesty and truth, few people ever get to encounter so regularly.

It really is something beautiful and, along with these stunning comments that you all keep posting, I have never felt so widely cared for and appreciated in all my life.

I wish me and Mr Luke Eemia had never met but these are truly special and incredible days. It would be great if it was something everyone reading this blog could experience.

Basically, what I'm trying to say is just please don't feel sorry for me - I'm having a great time!

After finishing up in 1535 the hard-core crowd sauntered up to Revolution in the centre of town for vodka and cocktails.

Huddersfield is not exactly buzzing on a Tuesday night but we all loved it.

Finally got to bed about 3.30am.

Thanks again to everyone who came out and for all the good times.

COMMENTS (54)

You have dragged me out of momentary introspection on days when running a house with three small energetic normal, demanding and crazy little boys have made me frustrated, into a frame of mind that has made me more appreciative of the charming normality that I have. Thank you! I will register. Don't stop blogging yet. *Ruth*

Dude, you absolutely rock. I can't believe life can have the audacity to suck so badly, or that a person can have the good grace and humour to deal with it so fantastically. *Heidi*

DETERIORATION
June 9, 2008

I'm trying to fight it but my bone marrow is malfunctioning big time.

The campaign and the petition are flying (laters Forsyth) and this could be a very interesting week - watch this space.

As for me, the disease is now starting to become more and more obvious.

My energy levels are terrible because I am not making enough red blood cells to carry oxygen around my body.

I can't focus and I'm noticeably more sluggish than I should be.

Getting up feels like I'm lying under a cover of rubble that needs strength I no longer have to lift from me.

But I still get up and I still keep going.

Visually it is alarming to actually see that my blood is no longer clotting as it should.

All over my left arm I have little bruises that look like a rash.

On the sides of my mouth there are dark patches where there have been bleeds that are still just healing.

I don't get nose bleeds but at the back of my throat I can smell blood constantly.

My chest is still infected and I seem to have picked up a sore throat.

Week on week this is getting harder.

I'm not finished yet though.

Tomorrow I will be in hospital all day having a couple of bags of blood and hopefully some platelets too.

This should pick me up a bit.

Comments (143)

Every time I see you on TV or hear your name I think 'thank God he is still here'. There are no words that can ever begin to explain what your inspirational attitude means to so many people. I have told friends, neighbours, colleagues to read your blog and many have been in tears. If ever there was a person to aspire to it is you. I have had a client in today who is 19 and alcoholic. He is desperate to get help and I used you and your story as an inspiration to him. He was in tears. You may well have saved his life. *Marion*

I did my assemblies this week to my pupils in Cardiff. They were visibly moved by your incredible story and self-less determination. Many of them have looked at this blog and continue to discuss and ask questions in school. I know that this has had a lasting affect on them and as citizens of the future they will remember. *Alan*

Sudders does Prime Minister's question time and Natasha Kaplinsky

June 10, 2008

I might be crumbling and fighting to stay alive but this has to go down as another incredible day.

Despite suggesting to you all that you 'watch this space' even I have to say I wasn't quite prepared for how well it all came together.

If you haven't already, watch this.

(Video shows Gordon Brown saluting Adrian - "Mr Sudbury" - and promising help for the campaign.)

I must confess to being a bit of a political geek and I always try and watch Prime Minister's Question Time.

For those of you who don't live in the UK it's basically a weekly meeting in the House of Commons where members of all our political parties have the opportunity to grill the Prime Minister on a range of subjects.

As you can see our campaign has now been highlighted at the highest level and I was personally referred to in the house by Gordon Brown.

It was bloody brilliant.

While all this was going on I was being driven down to the Sky News studios for an interview with the lovely Natasha Kaplinsky.

In our industry you are never quite sure how these celebrities are going to be.

Journalism teaches you to go in with an open mind - but she was absolutely charming.

She had lots of time for me and we were chatting off camera for ages.

Natasha even backed our campaign and signed the petition too.

We hit it off really well and it all seemed very genuine. I wished her well with her pregnancy and she even said she would look into joining the bone marrow register after she had given birth.

I'm updating the blog on my way home to Sheffield on the train - emailing text from my phone.

This will probably be my last big media outing.

I'm exhausted, coughing and spluttering, but what a day!

I have written before about going down in a blaze of glory and it feels just like that.

My friend Ashley even treated me to Champagne and canapés at St Pancras station!

Yesterday's two bags of blood and platelets have helped me feel better and made this wonderful day viable.

Let us never forget, it is the kindness of these strangers, and my 30-year-old donor from Germany, who have really made all this possible.

This post is for you.

COMMENTS (98)

Remember, it's not how long you live, but how best you live those years. I may live for 100 plus years but I may not achieve anything in life. But you in your short life are achieving great things. *Fr. Bosco Gall*

You are my idol! I would love to meet you! I am also very ill and if I read your stories it helps me to get better! *Clemens, Austria*

THIS LATEST AWARD I DEDICATE TO MY BEAUTIFUL SISTER (NOW WITH VIDEO AND SPECIAL REPORT BY ROOKIE REPORTER KEITH SUDBURY)

June 13, 2008

Despite being in such difficult times I have even more good news to share with you all.

To round off an exceptional week Baldy's Blog has won another prestigious award.

I have been named as the Press Gazette's multi-media journalist of the year, at their regional press awards.

There is a video of my parents collecting the award. It actually brought a little tear to my eye.

In our industry this is a huge accolade and it's one I'm absolutely delighted to receive.

But this post is for my amazing sister Carrie.

This latest one takes Baldy's Blog's tally to four.

Coming back to the blaze of glory reference, there are not many more awards a journalist like me can win.

God I wish I'd never got ill but the recognition for this little project has been unbelievable.

It's already scooped a Yorkshire Press Award, an award from the National Guild of Health Writers and the international Weblog Award - in Las Vegas!

The do was held at lunch time today at the Lancaster Hotel in London.

I knew I had been shortlisted but after Wednesday every day is just getting more and more difficult.

My chest feels like it is burning. It's really tight, dry and rattling.

As you can hear on my interviews my voice is struggling too and conserving energy is increasingly difficult.

My editor had already invited my parents to attend the ceremony so I asked them if they would go and represent me.

I had something else to take care of.

Last week it was Carrie's 24th birthday.

It was a brilliant day and her boyfriend Ian proposed to her.

She accepted and it was lovely seeing her with such a smile on her face.

All my family are devastated at what is happening but I feel really sorry for Carrie. It's so unfair that she is losing her brother.

We have always been close and the only time I get angry about my disease is when I think I won't be there for her wedding or be an uncle to her children.

I have seen with my own eyes that families move on but they never quite 'get over' such a painful and unnecessary loss.

Me and Carrie had arranged to go birthday shopping and go out for lunch.

It was great being able to treat her to some killer shoes, perfume and a slap up meal.

But more importantly it was just great spending quality time with her.

A disease and prognosis like mine eats into families much like the cancer itself. It's devastating and destructive in equal measures.

Despite knowing how proud they are of me for everything I have done and for dealing with this situation as best I can, it doesn't make their inevitable loss any easier to bear.

I love my sister and thinking about her getting so upset is heartbreaking.

Much like giving two fingers up to leukaemia I suppose all we can do, while I'm still able to function, is to enjoy ourselves and try and create more and more lasting memories.

They never die.

We had a great time today but I just wish this didn't have to come to an end.

Awards report by Keith Sudbury (my dad).

Please note additional story about my editor that mysteriously did not make it into the Huddersfield Examiner's report.

Keith speaks: "My first impression was how formal and prestigious the event was, so my new suit and expensive St Tropez shirt was just the ticket.

Free drinks were circulating all the time with bubbly, red, white and beer.

Mum and I were on table 17 with other members of the Mirror Group. There was a superb three course lunch with more wine constantly being served.

Pity I was driving, but mum was OK, although we were both struggling with loss of sense of taste and smell due to the worst cold I have had for years!

Just as an aside, I woke up two nights ago feeling terrible, and it did give me some insight into what Adrian has endured 1,000 times worse and for much, much longer.

Nick Ferrari was an excellent host. Very professional and kept the event moving along at a cracking pace.

Anyway back to the award. When Adrian's win was announced, his introduction was very good and very sincere.

I had forgotten that Adrian had done a 'piece to camera' and that was shown as we were on the stage having already having been introduced as 'brave parents'.

Adrian made a comment about a hard afternoon with Natasha Kaplinsky went down a storm, and there was a spontaneous standing ovation which was both fantastic and emotional.

We had our photos taken with Nick receiving the award and was then asked whether I wanted to say anything.

Now I know that you all take the p*ss out of me about 45 minute speeches (a little harsh I think!) but I had to say something, so I very quickly spoke of Adrian's campaign for a compulsory one hour sixth form lesson to educate and how they could all genuinely help you by going to your blog and signing the petition.

Mum and I were applauded all the way back to our seats. I wish Adrian could have been there because we were two proud parents.

At the end of the ceremony Nick came to speak with us and I must say, cynic that I am, he was charming and sincere.

The chairman of the panel of judges also came to speak with us and said it was a unanimous decision and on journalistic merits and not emotion.

Many people came up to mum and I at the end to say how inspirational Adrian has been.

We were then invited to the pub for drinks with Roy Wright (Examiner editor) and Neil Benson (Trinity Mirror's regional editorial director).

As we left the ceremony, Roy said rather than carry the heavy glass award around, he would put it into his rucksack.

Two to three drinks later Roy invited us to share his taxi, and as we sped towards St Pancras Station I casually asked Roy if he had picked up his rucksack.

Long story short, and dramatic U-turn, we retrieved the said object which was still on the pavement outside the pub!

Well a brilliant day came to an end. Well done again!"

Keith out.

COMMENTS (68)

Huge congratulations are in order for your most recent award! It is a terrible shame that these have been awarded under such circumstances but you truly have done a fantastic job of raising awareness, and removing the fear and stigma of 'cancer'. I'm sure there are many fellow sufferers going through the same who have been comforted by your blog and bravery. *Caroline*

So glad you took time out for your sister. *Anonymous*

Just a quick thought that your blog should be published in a book and the proceeds put towards publicity for the cause. Best of luck. *Henny*

Congratulations on ANOTHER award. Carrie congrats on your fabulous news. Look forward to meeting you with Adrian when I'm back. *Kate*

HEAD FUNK
June 15, 2008

In many ways this is an incredibly difficult post to write because I know it will raise hope that is misplaced.

Just before shopping with Carrie on Friday I got a phone call from the hospital.

More results had come back from my last bone marrow sample revealing why the Glivec drug or Imatinib had failed to work.

It also showed a drug from the same family, called Dasatinib, should be effective against my leukaemia.

They asked me to come in urgently, but as I had killer shoes, perfume and pizza to take care of, our little meeting had to wait.

At the moment I feel terrible.

I don't need to be stabbed by a nurse to tell you that my blood counts are poor.

This means I am not making enough red blood cells to carry a satisfactory amount of oxygen around my body.

Consequently I just feel exhausted. My eyes are heavy and even getting out of bed is becoming more and more challenging.

Blood blisters are forming in my mouth and occasionally I can taste blood throughout the day.

Thankfully, there have been no major bleeds yet

I will need blood and platelets again tomorrow or Tuesday.

This is the way of things and I was quite resigned to my fate.

However, in many ways, Friday's news was as cruel as it was kind.

My medical team had no choice but to pass this news onto me.

Without getting into the science too much the classic form of chronic myeloid leukaemia (CML) can now be controlled, with much success, by the drug Imatinib.

I've never had CML but a strange myelo-proliferative disorder which the doctors have never really come across before and have never quite known what to do with.

Before my bone marrow transplant there had been some success with Imatinib. My strange disease had responded and was improving - but the medical team were convinced my best option was a bone marrow transplant.

When traces returned earlier this year there was no reason to suggest that the Imatinib wouldn't be successful again.

Obviously this was incorrect.

The reason is that my particular strain of the disease has developed resistance to the drug.

Tests carried out on my last bone marrow sample show that it will be sensitive to this other drug Dasatinib.

Again, the consultants find themselves in uncharted territory.

There is no one else to compare with exactly how this drug is going to work in me - if at all.

But of course the doctors have to try and so do I.

The head funk is that it raises this slim, tiny, glimmer of hope that we can achieve a remission.

Because it's so unknown what is going to happen anything is technically possible.

But the likelihood of this, considering the extent to which the leukaemia has returned, is verging on the impossible.

The theory is the new drug will inhibit the cells that are misbehaving in my bone marrow.

Whether this can reverse all the damage that has been done is highly unlikely.

And then this in turn raises more almost unanswerable questions.

At the moment, as well as all the other vast quantities of infection fighting tablets, I am taking very mild chemotherapy tablets to slow down the cancer's progression.

Problems can occur if too many white blood cells get into the blood stream thickening it up.

The idea my consultants have is that this drug will make a better job of this so look on it as a preferred medicine in respect of palliative care.

I have had a great time recently but I am spiralling downwards.

I'm all for prolonging my life - obviously - but not if I'm feeling like this. Another six months of being bed ridden is not what I need at all.

Maybe these drugs will have no effect.

But what if they did start to reverse things?

On one level that would be fantastic, but realistically my leukaemia has survived so much, and already developed resistance to one member of this drug family.

From a scientific point of view it is therefore more than conceivable that resistance could develop again.

I've talked to my parents about my funeral, made plans - how could I cope with getting better only to have to go through all that again?

If I get rid of the leukaemia then it's back to living long-term with Graft versus Host Disease and a very poor quality of life.

Realistically nothing changes.

This is not the miracle people have been praying for.

But it's horrible trying to explain this complex haematological situation because you can see people's eyes light up with the aforementioned misplaced hope.

Emotionally, I wish I'd never had that phone call.

COMMENTS (58)

No one knows what effect the new drug will have on your particular form of leukaemia. Surely it's worth a go? *Anonymous*

Miracles can happen. You are clearly an exceptional human being, as many people have said, and it might just be that this drug is the miracle you're waiting for. *Mark*

My gut reaction on reading your latest blog was "Go for it Adrian!" *Margaret*

This glimmer of hope could be great, although you are aware of the knock on effect it can have on you. You have been through so much for someone so young physically and emotionally. Keep positive, there is a lot of love out there for you. *Rachel*

You already hit the one in a trillion lotto by getting two forms of this horrible disease; maybe that slim hope this drug offers will make a real difference. *Embi, Australia*

A glimmer of hope has been handed to you after you have set your mind to dealing with the inevitable. It is your body and your leukaemia and YOUR decision about what path to take. It is what you want and not what you think everyone else expects you to do. *Anonymous*

I think you and all that you achieved are brilliant and I've been searching for something really witty/comforting to say to make you smile and let you know how much you have touched me. I've got nothing. *Anonymous*

Keep fighting. As Winston Churchill said - 'Success is not final. failure is not fatal, it is the courage to continue that counts.' *Anonymous*

Don't give up now - you have too much still to do. *George*

Good luck and if there is a God then the outcome will be the right one whatever your choice. *Richard*

Adrian, the mind is a powerful thing, if anyone can do this it's you! All the luck in the world. *Jill*

CAN YOU HELP SUPPORT TWO GREAT BLOKES AND TWO GREAT CHARITIES?

June 15, 2008

Every day is getting harder now.

I'm going to need some sort of hospital attention either today or tomorrow.

My eyes are struggling to read what I'm writing, the exhaustion brought on by the anaemia runs so deep and is seemingly insurmountable and finally I have started having, dull drawn-out headaches.

The last problem could be due to a number of reasons but I fear it is linked to the new drug Dasatinib which I started taking over the weekend.

My hands are shaking a little bit as I sip my glass of water and dread the impending number of tablets I've got to get into me.

My resting heart rate, writing this in bed, is over 115 beats a minute as it struggles to push the limited blood and oxygen supply around my body.

The good news is that on Friday my consultant prescribed some new antibiotics which have really helped clear my chest.

My croaky voice, you may have heard in the previous post, looks like it is improving.

Let's be honest - this is a dreadful, maybe even tragic, situation that I find myself in.

But every day checking the comments that are now flooding in from all over the world is such a support.

I am sorry that I am incapable of replying to you all but know that all your voices, often of complete strangers, wishing me, my family and friends well, is a mountain of comfort.

It's great being part of this global community and I suppose in many ways we are all in this together now. Sorry about that!

Again thank you to you all.

Have a look at what Ben and Olie are planning too - see online video.

SIGN UP AND MAYBE SAVE A LIFE
June 16, 2008

You could become a lifesaver this week - by signing up as a bone marrow donor.

As part of Adrian's campaign to recruit more bone marrow donors to the register, the Examiner has arranged clinics where people can call in and sign up.

The first - organised with the Anthony Nolan Trust - will be held at Huddersfield Methodist Mission on Lord Street on Wednesday (June 18) from 2pm to 7pm.

Adrian is urging people to go along and sign up. "You have a wonderful and unique opportunity to save someone else's life, not just here in the UK, but anywhere on the planet.

"Over 16,000 people worldwide are waiting to find a bone marrow match. Without one these mothers, sisters, brothers, wives and husbands will die. With your help maybe they don't have to.

"I'm grateful for the incredible way everyone in Huddersfield has got behind the Examiner's campaign already."

He said people are often reluctant to sign up because they believe they would have to undergo an horrific and dangerous procedure if they were a match for someone who needed a transplant. But in fact, the procedure is safe - there is no spine drilling or risk of paralysis - and in most cases, it is not too dissimilar to giving blood.

Adrian said: "Bone marrow donation is not the scary procedure everyone thinks it is. If you don't believe me, please have a look at the videos on this blog under the recent entry 'A plea for more bone marrow donors'."

Each person who attends the clinic will be asked to fill in a form and will have a small sample of blood taken for tissue typing.

You can sign up to be a donor if you are aged between 18 and 40 and in good health.

You should be prepared to stay on the register until the age of 60 and be happy to keep the Anthony Nolan Trust informed of changes to your contact details and circumstances, such as health problems.

There will be another Anthony Nolan Trust/Examiner clinic at Huddersfield Town Hall on July 8 from 2pm to 7pm. Kirklees Council has donated the town hall reception room free of charge - so thanks to them.

There will also be a donor registration clinic on July 27 at the Galpharm Stadium, from 11.30am to 2.30pm. This clinic has been organised by the

Examiner and the National Blood Service, which keeps the other UK bone marrow donor register.

Their rules are slightly different. You can sign up to the National Blood Service register - known as the British Bone Marrow Register - if you are aged 18 to 49 and in good health. But to join this register, you must be eligible to be a blood donor.

Simply drop in to the clinic and make sure you ask the nurse about being put on the register at the beginning of the session. A small sample of blood will be taken for tissue typing, then the main blood donation will begin. Even if you are too young to or too old to become a bone marrow donor, you can still give blood at the session if you are aged 17 to 59.

A special note here to all the gay men who have posted comments on this blog, saying how much they'd like to be allowed to sign up as bone marrow donors. Now you can! The Anthony Nolan Trust recently changed its policy. Previously, gay men had been excluded from becoming donors, because they were deemed at high risk of carrying blood-borne diseases. Now, anyone gay or straight can join as a donor - as long as they do not engage in 'high risk' practices which could leave them exposed to disease, such as sharing needles or having unprotected sex.

Please note though, the National Blood Service has not yet changed its policy on gay men - so if you're in this category and want to sign up, make sure it's an Anthony Nolan Trust clinic you attend.

IMPORTANT: You only have to be on one register, as both are searched when a patient needs a bone marrow transplant.

COMMENTS (15)

Hi there, I'm very impressed by the work Adrian has been doing to encourage more bone marrow donors. It's an amazingly selfless thing to do when faced with limited time. In 2001 I donated bone marrow through stem cell collection after several years on the Anthony Nolan register. I found the process fairly straightforward and I'm certain it's a lot less painful than suffering leukaemia or other illness dependent on a stem cell donation as a cure. If you are able to give blood then stem cell collection is very similar, it just takes up a bit more of your time. Prior to the collection, injections are given over a few days - painless, but left me feeling a bit fatigued and that was all. I hope all Adrian's efforts really make a difference as that would be the least any of us could do to help. Go on, join the register, it's not that difficult! *Julie, Leeds*

THE CAMPAIGN: PLEASE DO NOT FUDGE A DYING MAN'S WISH (PLUS GARY LINEKER)
June 16, 2008

It's time to update everyone on the campaign.

My call again is to introduce a talk to all second year sixth form students about blood, bone marrow and organ donation.

That age is key because our young adults can make an informed decision about whether this is something they would like to help out with.

I'm in the media and let's face it - this is what happens at the moment.

A pretty toddler needs a match, or some ugly bugger like me hits the headlines, and maybe a couple of hundred people join the bone marrow register or donate blood - but then the issue fades.

Not good enough.

As we have all recently learnt there are over 16,000 people worldwide waiting for a bone marrow transplant.

Without one they will die.

This campaign will change all that because I am convinced a steady stream of young adults will decide that donation, of all kinds, is something they want to be a part of.

First, the good news.

Health Secretary Alan Johnson and Education Secretary Ed Balls, sent a joint letter to me announcing that this talk will be rolled out nationally from September - but only for 14 to 15-year-olds.

That is fabulous.

But my message to the Government is please do not do this half-arsed. A second talk has to be part of the sixth form curriculum when people can choose to become donors if they so wish.

I have always felt strongly about this but now I can't let it go.

I'm not one for Bob Geldolf style ranting but please indulge me for the next few sentences.

How many times do we hear in the media that Britain is looking at adopting the Scandinavian model for such and such, the American system for that, the Australian model for the other?

Here we have a chance to have the best educated young adults in the world about donation through two very simple talks.

For once Britain could be a world leader in this and for once other countries will look upon us with envious eyes.

As you can see from our Prime Minister this is now a "priority" for the Department of Health.

The scheme that will be rolled out from September is called Give and Let Live.

It was being piloted at a number of schools when I met Mr Johnson so I don't think our campaign has had any effect on this. It may of course help speed up matters.

I think this is excellent news and I really am pleased with how receptive the Government has been.

But it can't stop there.

Give and Let Live could quite easily be expanded, through the citizenship scheme, into sixth forms too. All it needs to be is revamped and put into a more adult context.

I imagine it as more of a discussion, something that many people at that age would really engage with.

In response to the campaign I have been overwhelmed by not only the level of support for this, but also the huge number of organisations that are willing to help out.

So there are people to lead these discussions, materials in place albeit for a younger audience and the costs will be minimal.

I can see no reason why this can't happen.

As I've said before this is not about forcing people to do anything they don't want.

It's about giving our future generations the ability to make an educated and informed choice.

I've learnt so much about bone marrow and blood donation.

For example, if you are gay you are not allowed in the UK to donate blood. That's a decision I disagree with - I would sooner have the blood from a monogamous homosexual than a promiscuous heterosexual any day - but that's a different issue.

But if you are gay you CAN join a bone marrow register through the Anthony Nolan Trust.

As pointed out by reader Yvette Price-Mear in the UK we have two different donor registers.

The Anthony Nolan Trust accept people from 18 to 40.

The one through the National Blood Service, just ask the next time you give blood, runs from 18 to 49.

When I used to give blood I thought it was only going to be used in Accident and Emergency or maybe surgery.

Blood is used throughout hospital departments - I must have received in excess of 60 bags of blood throughout my treatment - 'grateful' does not not even begin to justify this kindness.

People think bone marrow donation is horrific and it is not.

Just how much confusion is out there on these matters?

I say again, all this misinformation could be changed by two talks to our young adults.

One at 14/15 - brilliant.

But it HAS to be revisited at 17/18.

Two talks, minimal cost and a transformation of how people think about donating.

Please Prime Minister, Mr Johnson and Mr Balls - do not fudge this dying man's wish.

In other news the campaign has received cross-party support.

Liberal Democrat leader Nick Clegg, who also happens to be a Sheffield MP, said: "It is extremely important to raise public awareness about bone marrow donation. We must do all we can to ensure people know the potential of bone marrow donation for saving lives."

Conservative Shadow Health Secretary Andrew Lansley said: "Adrian Sudbury has shown extraordinary courage throughout his campaign. I fully support his aim to raise awareness about bone marrow donations. As many people as possible should be encouraged to sign up for the register on a voluntary basis, if they are in a position to do so."

And finally...

Health-wise it was platelets today, a lot of sleeping, and a random bit of vomiting.

What was particularly unpleasant was that as I was sick the force was such that it felt like my eyeballs were going to burst.

Spots of blood appeared on my eyelids and I can just about see correctly now. Nice one.

Ranting and stuff over, let's get to the interesting bit.

Tomorrow at around 10am GMT (Tuesday, June 17) I'm going back on 5Live (a national radio station) to speak with the host Victoria Derbyshire and England football legend Gary Lineker.

He is a true gentleman of the sport and I believe never picked up a booking in his professional career.

I will always remember the last time I cried at a football match. I was nine and England lost to West Germany in the Italia '90 World Cup.

Lineker was outstanding in the tournament.

Anyway, he is interested in the campaign because his son suffered with leukaemia as a child. Thankfully he got through it, but I'm sure the former England striker will have lots to say on the subject and will lend a lot of weight to what I hope to achieve.

Listen out for any amusing Bob Geldolf style rants from me.

You can hear it live on the internet but if you miss it we will try and stick on the audio later tomorrow.

COMMENTS (25)

My goodness… as usual, your bravery and strength make my heart swell with respect. Have a great week, Adrian! *Devon*

Adrian, you continue to amaze me with your words and spirit. Know that you are thought of daily here in the States. Your campaign is exactly what we need in every country. Stay strong! Have a Happy Day, *Alyce, California, USA*

FALLING BACK TO MY PARENTS, FAMILY AND LOVED ONES
June 19, 2008

We have been through quite a lot together now but I imagine for many of you this post will make for uncomfortable reading.

We have journeyed through the ups and downs of leukaemia, its treatments, living and dying.

There have been a few laughs in between the infertility, my fiancee leaving me, my skin crumbling off and the recent death sentence.

Lavish award ceremonies, outrageous media tarting and all of us being involved in a massive campaign that will hopefully benefit thousands of people around the world for years to come.

But a time comes when you have to be honest with yourself.

After last night's shenanigans it's time to sacrifice a bit more of my independence and move back in with my parents.

Time to catch up.

We are never going to know exactly but it looks like I am reacting very badly to the new drug Dasatinib.

Thanks to everyone who posted their experiences about this medicine.

I started taking these new pills on Friday and by Saturday was having piercing headaches.

Not only that but I vomited twice on consecutive days.

Obviously, having had the pleasure of being sick on quite a number of occasions over the last 18 months, this wouldn't normally bother me too much.

But I have never experienced anything like it.

The pressure and velocity was such that it felt like my eye balls were going to burst out of my head.

All over my eyelids were spots of blood caused by minor internal bleeding.

The worst thing was that it gave me what looked like two black-eyes.

They really hurt, were starting to swell up, and I was struggling to see out of them for days.

Friends came and stayed but it was becoming increasingly difficult to ignore.

Last night my parents looked after me in Sheffield.

The headache was getting out of control and, determined to avoid a stay in hospital, I suggested we try out of hours doctors service.

The first doctor rolls up, now whether this is due to a language barrier I don't know, but I asked him if he was prescribing pain relief. He said yes and injected it into my arm.

I should add that he seemed rather keen to make the injection into my buttocks.

I challenged this and the arm was then deemed acceptable.

Turns out though he gave me a sedative leading me to wake up in the middle of the night, ranting, babbling and devouring two bowls of fruit.

That, it turns out, is how mental I get.

The headache returned, and having had these sorts of extreme pains on the ward, I know the only answer is something along the lines of morphine.

The second doctor eventually appears, prescribes the drug, but there is nowhere to collect it until the pharmacies open about three hours later.

Great out of care service guys.

So despite everything my dad ends up driving me into the Royal Hallamshire Hospital again for treatment.

Unsurprisingly, the morphine always slips down quite well and within about 20 minutes I was feeling a lot better.

But my head was now swelling up on the underside and around the jaw.

Apparently this could be caused by a small blockage meaning blood is not returning correctly.

I'm run down, exhausted, cannot stop coughing and have a massively swollen head.

Here is a bit of irony for you though, one doctor suggested treating this new facial swelling with steroids!

Seriously, he described it as maybe helping to clear the blockage and returning things to normal.

The nurses were so worried this morning that they were concerned I wasn't going to make it until next week.

After this evening - apart from the massively irritating cough and vanity issues - I reckon I've got a bit more time left than that.

I'm hoping friends and family will break up visits and come throughout the week.

I have also got some excellent palliative care medicines at my disposal too which means there should be no more repeat performances of last night.

COMMENTS (176)

Hi Adrian, so sorry to hear you're feeling so rough. You are in my thoughts and prayers and hopefully you will be feeling better very soon. Best Wishes Nikki ;) *Nicola*

Adrian, no words... just thinking of you and your family. Take care. *Diane*

POST TRANSPLANT COMPLICATIONS
June 21, 2008

Thanks again for every single incredible comment that is being posted. I really want to reply to you all but I am just not capable of doing it.

I just want you to know I read them all in the morning, throughout the day, and often at night too.

My doctor, and excellent local medical team, were speaking to me about it yesterday and I said: "How can all these positive thoughts from all over the planet not be lifting my spirits?"

I think they all understood.

The morphine derivative is helping control my headache and cough. The ridiculous mumps-like swelling is also starting to subside.

More great news about the campaign is on the cards too. Will give you all the details for a major event in London either tomorrow or first thing on Monday.

This post is really for fellow 'post bone marrow transplanters'.

It's been written for quite a while and is really a round-up of all the post-transplant complications I have encountered since being released from isolation.

I thought it might be useful for people who have undergone the same process.

However, as the doctors keep reminding me, everyone is different and you never know what is around the corner.

Remember, some people will encounter very few problems - if any at all.

Transplants do work and provide an excellent cure for many bone marrow disorders.

Firstly my tablets.

After a bone marrow transplant you have effectively wiped out your immune system and need to grow it again.

You also need to give your new developing immune system time to adjust to your body. Because of this you need drugs that suppress your immune response that are slowly tapered down.

The drug I had is called Cyclosporin.

The following tablets are taken as prophylactics – medicines that help prevent infection before one takes hold.

Erythromycin: An antibiotic which is effective against a whole range of bacteria.

Voriconazole: An antifungal agent. When I had pneumonia last year this was caused by a fungal spore that was either from a plant or just knocking around in my lungs.

Acyclovir: An antiviral agent.

All these tablets are taken at 10am and 10pm.

After my initial release from hospital my main symptoms were nausea and tiredness. I was absolutely shattered and can remember thinking I was never going to get stronger.

It was different to straightforward chemotherapy. I seemed to bounce back quite quickly after that. This was much tougher. I remember after a couple of weeks I would be making progress, then feel rough again. It was a case of two steps forward - one step back.

Sometimes I would just randomly be sick. Eat some food, or even the tablets, and it would just set off that vomit mechanism. My stomach felt a lot more delicate all of the time and my appetite was poor.

Had a few beers one night and then was just sick.

Anti-sickness tablets from the hospital helped.

They say the average transplant patient will be back in three times with infections and that's exactly right for me.

The first two were in the summer and directly linked to my Hickman line. Each time I would be at home and start to get that freezing sensation that goes hand in hand with a fever.

On both occasions I was in hospital for the best part of a week while antibiotics took care of the infection.

The last one is the "cold" that brought me back in for another week prior to Christmas.

With the exception of Graft versus Host Disease - which I've written about extensively - they were the most serious problems but I suppose all to be expected.

Here are some of the weirder things I encountered.

Hair growth
It took ages to come back and then came back in some crazy places – like on my cheeks. The steroids then seemed to make it grow in a peculiar way too. It's coming back now but darker and thicker.

Acne
At one point my skin broke out in what looked like acne. Doctors said it was probably linked to over active hair follicles. This was - thankfully - treated with a short course of tablets.

Fingers and toes
While on the steroids the edges of some of my fingers and toes developed infections. It was quite painful for a while and made walking incredibly difficult. This was treated with an antibiotic called Clindamycin. Fingers seemed to catch on everything.

Also connected to the steds were unbelievable pains in the middle of the night. These included crazy cramps in my feet an intense pain in my bones. A reminder that these drugs can seriously damage your joints and bones. I also found I needed to take a leak at 4 or 5am every day.

People in our situation do feel like we rattle after taking so many drugs on a regular basis.

The steroids are still taken at around 8am in the morning.

I am often reminded of the old song "I know an old lady who swallowed a fly."

GvHD leads to steds which increase chance of infections so in turn you need more antibiotics.

The steds also mean you need to take Lanzoprazole to protect the lining of your stomach.

Cyclosporin caused my blood pressure to rocket so yet more tablets were required to keep this under control.

I was also taking Glivec until I relapsed.

That is quite a pharmacy to be carrying around on visits - not to mention the E45 and moisturising creams for the dry skin.

The latest.

Now being in a palliative setting the game changes slightly.

I have stopped taking Glivec - obviously.

Disatinib - the potential 'miracle cure' which caused me to be sick, gave me splitting headaches, internal eye bleeding and the bottom half of my face to bloat up like Desperate Dan - has also, funnily enough, been stopped.

The mild tablet chemotherapy hydroxyurea has been sent back to the pharmacist.

As have the antibiotics.

This leaves me with steroids, cyclosporin, voriconazole and acyclovir. I am also coming off the anti-depressant fluoxetine because, I have said many times before, I know I'm not depressed, just have a lot on my plate to deal with.

Although this post is a bit flat I wanted to squeeze it in because it's a good reference point for people going through a similar time.

Best wishes to you all and thanks again for your continued support.

COMMENTS (109)

All the best mate. Truly, you are one of the few people who has genuinely made a positive difference to the world with your ceaseless campaigning. Long may your words stand as a beacon to everyone affected by this terrible, terrible illness. You can leave people any number of material goods, but if you don't leave them a good example then you leave them nothing. You, my friend, have left the world a great amount. *Dan*

Hi Adrian! You've articulated what happens post transplant in a clear and succinct way. As a former microbiologist, I'm dead impressed about your knowledge of antivirals, antifungals and antibiotics. All this aside though, I am glad you are hanging in there and I will be sending a lot more positive thoughts and prayers your way. Can't wait to read your post on Monday for the big reveal. *Elizabeth*

WESTMINSTER TO HOST A HUGE BONE MARROW DRIVE
June 22, 2008

This is an incredible coup for our campaign to educate all second year sixth form students about blood, bone marrow and organ donation.

On Wednesday afternoon all our MPs and staff who work within the complicated network surrounding the House of Lords and Commons, will be invited to attend a unique event in the Jubilee Room.

As far as I understand nothing on this scale, in this venue, has ever been done before.

I'm really excited about it because for those MPs and staff who are under 40 they will be able to sign up directly to the bone marrow register.

The clinic will be on Wednesday after Prime Minister's Question Time (around 12.30pm).

It is thought to be the first time a bone marrow donor clinic has ever been held in Parliament, although other health clinics and blood donation sessions have been held there before.

It has been organised by the ever-impressive Colne Valley MP Kali Mountford.

I wonder if any of you reading this can help?

Could you get onto your MPs, let them know about Wednesday's event, and if they are under 40, ask them to consider having a small blood sample taken and joining the register. Even if they are too old - let them know about the blog, the campaign and let's all work together to make this happen.

All we need to do is keep the pressure on.

Prime Minister Gordon Brown and the health and education secretaries have "backed" this campaign, as have Tory Shadow Health Secretary Andrew Lansley and Lib-Dem leader Nick Clegg.

Now let's see if they really do.

Hopefully Mr Balls and Mr Johnson will be able to give more commitments about expanding the education to that crucial sixth form age where our young adults will be able to actually donate blood and join marrow registers.

I think this is going to be an incredible event right in the heart of the corridors of power. I am thrilled that Kali Mountford and the Anthony Nolan Trust have organised such a high profile event.

Campaign packs will also be available so that MPs can set up similar events in their own constituencies. At the clinic, a film made by the Anthony Nolan Trust will be played showing me getting all Bob Geldolf again about why it is crucial that 17 and 18-year-olds are better educated.

The Government has already demonstrated how important this is to them by rolling out the Give and Let Live talks from September, educating all 14 to 15-year-olds about donation.

But without banging on again too much - oh here I go: "Two talks will transform how our young adults think about donation and I am convinced, if these are both implemented, other countries will look to Britain, for once, as being a world leader in this field."

COMMENTS (163)

How fabulous is that?! *Lacey*

VICTORY AT WESTMINSTER
June 25, 2008

I am delighted to tell you all that the campaign to get a compulsory talk to all second year sixth form students about blood, bone marrow and organ donation became one step closer to reality today.

Commitments have now been made from both our Secretaries of State for Health and Education, Alan Johnson and Ed Balls, that they are going to do everything they can to make this happen.

Thank you so much.

Britain will really lead the way in educating our young adults from this day forward.

I am absolutely thrilled and would again like to thank all of you wonderful readers for keeping up the pressure too.

Someone commented that this whole project, your determination to make this happen and the interactivity with all your parliamentary representatives, really restored a sense of democracy and being able to do something positive.

I could not agree more and it has been genuinely wonderful working with all of you on this.

I have to add too, how many people have cabinet ministers saying they have felt like they have been running your fan club for the past five weeks?!

The results from today's unprecedented event at Westminster include:

- Commitment to roll out the Give and Let Live Scheme to all 14/15-year-olds from September.
- It's too short notice to begin a similar talk in a more adult context for 17/18-year-olds from this September. But colleges and schools will be written to to take part in voluntary events. I know many of you are already but here is a great chance for you to express your support for this initiative by writing to the top people.
- If this proves successful, the talks can be developed and rolled out as part of the national curriculum for the following academic year.
- Several MPs and cabinet ministers gave a blood sample and joined the Anthony Nolan Trust's bone marrow register.
- Many more signed our petition and took away special packs explaining how to set up clinics in their own constituencies.

On general reflection I would say that was a success.

Once again massive thanks to Kali Mountford MP for making this all possible and legendary Huddersfield Examiner reporter Katie Campling who has worked so hard behind the scenes to pull this off.

Special report by Katie "Campers" Campling

Government ministers and MPs have signed up as bone marrow donors at a special clinic held in the House of Commons.

MPs, Westminster staff and even cabinet ministers visited the Anthony Nolan Trust (ANT) donor recruitment clinic in the Jubilee Room of the historic building.

The clinic was organised by Colne Valley MP Kali Mountford as part of the Examiner and Adrian Sudbury's campaign to recruit more donors to the register.

A key part of Adrian's campaign is to push the Government to ensure 17 and 18-year-olds are educated about donation as standard in schools and colleges.

This is the crucial age where young adults can give blood and join registers should they choose to do so.

A total of 14 people signed up as donors at the clinic - including cabinet ministers, Secretary of State for Work and Pensions James Purnell and Andrew Burnham, Secretary of State for Culture.

Mr Purnell said: "I was not really aware of bone marrow donation before Kali Mountford talked to me about it. But I think it's something I would be prepared to do."

You have to be aged 18 to 40 to sign up as a donor with the ANT.

Those ministers and MPs that were too old to become donors also had a chance to help, by signing the campaign's online petition, calling for better education about donation.

MPs signing it included Halifax MP Linda Riordan - whose son donated bone marrow five years ago - and Hull East MP Mark Tarmy, whose 10-year-old son underwent a bone marrow transplant for leukaemia last year.

He said: "It's very important. There's seven other kids in hospital, who were there with my son, who are still waiting for the phone to ring to say they have a transplant."

All attending MPs left with campaign material.

Dawn Primarolo, minister of state for public health, added her support.

She said: "This campaign is seriously impressive. He is inspiring people and getting the message across in a simple and understandable way. It is a privilege to be associated with it."

Health Secretary Alan Johnson and Ed Balls, Secretary of State for Children, Schools and Families also gave a speech at the event.

They met with Adrian back in May and have pledged their support for his campaign.

The Government's donation education programme, Give And Let Live, is due to be rolled out to 14 and 15-year-olds in schools from September.

But the ministers said they were still working hard to implement Adrian's wish, for older teenagers to be educated.

Mr Johnson said: "Since we met with Adrian, I could officially be described as the secretary of the Adrian Sudbury fan club and Ed is the chairman.

"Adrian made a real impression on us. I have never met anyone with the passion of Adrian. It was really, really inspirational.

"It is Adrian's passion that we get the message across to people as young as possible. Adrian is focused on the 17 to 18 year olds.

"We are talking to the Anthony Nolan Trust and we are really galvanised in our departments to see what more we can do. We will ensure that the Adrian Sudbury fan club delivers."

Mr Balls added: "It is a great pity that Adrian can't be here although we will all have the chance to go on his blog and see what he makes of it!

"You see from his writing and also when we met him the passion, purpose and determination that good things will come, come what may for Adrian.

"We are determined to do what we can to back him to make sure young people get the chance he is not going to have."

MPs can then try and spread the word in their own constituencies and set up their own clinics.

Mr Balls and Mr Johnson are writing to all schools in the UK over the summer, asking them to ensure the Give And Let Live scheme is implemented.

Kali Mountford said she was thrilled with the response to the clinic from her fellow MPs and ministers.

"There's more great work going on here today with the people who are signing up to the register. Without you this event would mean nothing at all. It means a great deal to Adrian and me."

Dewsbury MP Shahid Malik also signed up to the register yesterday. He said he plans to try and stir up interest in his constituents about the issue of bone marrow donation.

He himself is averse to needles, but said it was a fear worth overcoming in the name of a good cause.

"It has been a very powerful and incredibly brave thing that Adrian has decided to go and fight not for himself but for others.

"I will certainly over the coming weeks look to organise awareness events in Dewsbury. I want people to understand what's involved in being a donor and how it can save lives."

Even before the event happened today it was receiving media attention from Channel 4 News, AOL and a huge UK journalism website.

Please drop us a comment if you spot it anywhere else!

COMMENTS (99)

Well done Adrian, Brilliant news!! You really have started something that should have been up and running. I hope you can drink something special tonight to toast your success. *Em x*

That's just fantastic news - a great victory - and well done you for keeping up the pressure! I have been an avid reader of your blog for a few weeks now - and it's great to have some good news to read. You truly are an inspiration - long may you continue to inspire others! *Andy*

TIME FOR A QUICK CATCH UP

June 27, 2008

It's blood and platelets today to help keep me going.

I am worn down and smatterings of rash-like internal bleeds on the surface of the skin indicate I need some urgent attention.

Everything that has been achieved this week fills me with a sense of enormous pride and I have even more good news to share with you all.

But first, I noticed there have been a few requests to find out how I am doing.

The honest answer is each week it just gets that bit harder and harder.

My energy is low, the chest infection and cough are managed but not improving, I am generally tired but over the last couple of days I have grown particularly concerned about my legs.

This strange pain around my knees coupled with an uncomfortable sense of muscle weakness has started alarm bells ringing.

During my transplant I lost the use of my legs for about two days and we never really found out why.

The pain can be controlled but it's just whether they will continue to bear the weight of my body.

I will chat to the experts today and see if they have any answers or advice. I suspect steroids are probably at the heart of this little conundrum.

At the moment stairs are only a slight problem.

Although I accept I have lost a lot of independence by moving back more permanently with my parents it was without doubt the right decision and they have been absolutely terrific.

In my own flat I was slowly losing the ability to look after myself.

Pots remained unwashed, small piles of odd socks grew into mounds of dirty washing, milk and bread went mouldy.

Some would argue that there was not much difference between that and before I got ill.

However, to be back with my parents, in such a warm and loving environment, and to have all that taken care of, has actually enabled me to do much more with my time and energy.

To say they have been, and continue to be magnificent, is a massive understatement and I hope they know how grateful I am.

Although these continue to be 'challenging circumstances' I do not feel upset, scared or lonely.

In fact, we are all actually having a pretty incredible time.

My gradual death, as long as the quality of life remains reasonable, is actually quite a liberating experience.

We sort of have an open-door policy at the moment where friends and family give us a call the day before, check how I am, then just rock up.

It's honestly been great fun.

As you are beginning to see more and more, I have had nothing but the absolute privilege of sharing my time on this planet with some incredible people, from all different walks of life.

People bring food, drink, cake - sometimes my mum cooks up a big meal - but it just seems to work really well.

Through this method of hanging out we also get random groups of people, who wouldn't necessarily turn up together, coming over and getting on really well.

As I keep saying - don't feel sorry for me. I'm having a blast.

But I think this also applies to my parents who love seeing how much my friends care for me. They are also really great to get on with so I think they are enjoying the company immensely.

And now a little something from Milan.

A while ago I entered a European competition for the best cancer reporter. It wasn't really something I thought about winning because it was essentially about reporting breakthroughs in treatment and cutting edge research.

I got this email through from the judges yesterday.

"On behalf of the European School of Oncology and the judging panel for the 2008 Best Cancer Reporter Award I am pleased to inform you that you have won a Best Cancer Reporter Special Recognition Award.

"Although you did not win the main award, the judges were extremely impressed with your blog and the efforts you have made to raise awareness about the need for bone and marrow donations and wanted to acknowledge your tremendous work.

"You have clearly shown how powerful it can be when journalists, who are also patients, draw upon their communication skills to convey important messages to the public about issues that can have a huge impact on cancer patients.

"Congratulations on winning this special recognition award - we were very pleased that you were nominated and are delighted to be able to recognise your work."

Best wishes, Kathy Redmond, Co-ordinator, ESO Media Programme
Grazie molto!

COMMENTS (42)

Yet more accolades Adrian!!! Not only are you a star in our country, you are applauded in Europe for what you have achieved, and no doubt there will be more awards to come. In a very short time you have done more for bone marrow donation awareness than the experts have achieved in their working lives! Enjoy every moment of your success with your wonderful family and friends, and remember that you have such love and support from all your "blog" fan club. *Lots of love Sandra S*

Hi Adrian, congrats on yet another well deserved accolade! I have said before, you write about your condition in layman's terms and with a clarity that is so informative and easy to understand that I have directed many people to your blog to save me explaining lots of what is happening to Dan! So again, thank you for that help. I am so glad that you are 'having a blast' and it brings home that all our day to day worries re money, careers etc are insignificant. What is important are family, friends, respect and love for others and experiences, not material things - that's what brings happiness. Have you ever heard of Maslow's Hierarchy of Needs? Every human needs shelter, food and security as a basis to build a fulfilling life upon. I think you have all three in bucket loads. Also, the art of communication is the vital ingredient. So many people forget how to talk to each other. I think you have definitely nailed that one on the head as well! You have reached out to your global family and we have all responded. Love and hugs, *Sally x*

OBSTACLES WERE MADE FOR OVERCOMING

July 4, 2008

Well - every single one of you reading this is incredible too.

I am even more confident than ever that we are going to pull this off.

I have been discussing it all with Katie Campling from the Examiner and Caroline Berger from the Anthony Nolan Trust.

We have decided we have hit a hump rather than a brick wall.

I hoped that after everything we've worked to achieve - it's not much to ask - that Whitehall would now be able to wave a magic wand and make all this happen.

Basically, it is not as easy as you might assume for the Government to make the talk about blood, bone marrow and organ donation compulsory as such, for sixth form colleges and schools.

Colleges are not necessarily obliged to do it.

However, from September it was only going to be rolled out on a voluntary basis anyway.

Time is still on our side. We just need to get back to the drawing board and re-think a little bit.

If anyone out there is involved with further education colleges or sixth form schools, and thinks this is a good idea, you might have a better insight into how to make this more formal.

Please get in touch.

I still think if we reflect a little, seek a bit more advice, and please I include all of you in this, and work together, we can put so much pressure from the college end up and on the Government down, that many will have to look at this seriously.

That's roughly where we are now and I will keep you updated next week with more details.

As promised yesterday, there is lots more in the pipeline that will keep this campaign up and running.

A big call to the gay community.

Remember you do not have to be a blood donor to join the Anthony Nolan Trust's bone marrow register.

Huddersfield police officer Mark Carter was crowned Mr Gay UK in 2006.

He has backed our campaign and believes that more gay people - who are not allowed to give blood in the UK - would really like to donate bone marrow where they can.

He said: "I knew that gay men couldn't give blood, so I never thought about being a bone marrow donor either. It's something I would like to do now I know I can."

Rebecca Sedgwick, one of the charity's donor recruitment managers, said: "We now no longer refuse people to join on the grounds of their sexuality.

"We ask all people joining to be honest and exclude themselves if they are involved in high-risk sexual practices that may increase their risk of exposure to transmissible diseases."

If any of you know people who are gay, please forward this blog onto them and spread the word.

SUDDERS DOES THE HOUSE OF LORDS
July 7, 2008

Our campaign has now been highlighted in the House of Lords.

This is another massive boost for the campaign, petition and everything else we are trying to achieve.

There are few issues I am aware of that have worked their way up the political ladder so quickly and so spectacularly.

Thank you to Lord Harrison (of Chester) and Gordon Parsons (of Nottingham) for taking such an interest in what I am attempting to make a reality and for raising the issue of education on such an incredible stage.

My message to all the Lords reading this, or who have taken an interest in the issue, please get in touch if you have any further ideas about making this 40-minute talk about blood, bone marrow and organ donation, a reality in sixth form colleges.

While the exposure was superb - the answer was of course less clear.

We are still in the process of talking to colleges and developing a more detailed strategy.

So much for just hoping Whitehall would wave a magic wand.

It's such a simple, cost-effective idea, but I know it is going to take more time and work.

Thanks again for all the ideas that are bubbling under the surface and the general ground swell of support and assistance.

Please keep your thoughts and comments coming in.

Before I shuffle off I will make sure there is a clear strategy to ensure the talk comes off as effectively as it can, that the blog keeps going in some way and perhaps we set up a database/mailing list to all ensure in the coming years you are able to easily keep in touch and this issue is not forgotten.

I know my family and friends will not let this rest - and although it feels strange writing this - I include all of you as part of this group now.

Does that seem a bit strange to you too?

I have always joked that I'm not a technical person, or an internet user as such, just a print hack who got ill and wrote about it, but there are these powerful connections being built around the world, spanning the computers of strangers I feel like I have known for years yet have never met - and perhaps will never meet.

Sometimes when I take a step back I am just in awe at how incredible, powerful, and influential, this community has become.

I have written briefly, and on reflection will certainly revisit in a future post, the curious nature of how liberating my gradual demise has been.

But it has also been an incredibly empowering experience which, although I have undoubtedly generated myself, has been swept up vortex-like into something unique and seemingly verging on the invincible.

It's been an absolute privilege to share this ride - which I'm still trying to fully appreciate and assimilate - with everyone of you who reads this.

In other news.

Got battered again at the weekend.

I have had the pleasure of spending time with my Auntie Helen and Uncle Iain, Rachel, Ben, Phil, Emma (who cooked the most incredible Moroccan banquet on Saturday for us all), Olie, Tom, Zoey, Poppy, Katie, Sam, Jo and Gemma.

On Sunday we all got absorbed into that most compelling of Wimbledon finals.

My parents and I talk a lot and I can see in their eyes - and from the laughs we are all having together - that they are enjoying this wonderful company and support too.

It remains a disastrous time but at this precise moment are any of us unhappy?

The answer is a resounding no.

Of course all this fun is hard work but we are doing our best to keep up with the pace.

I like to think my day generally pans out into several roughly defined stages.
- Light fruit salad style breakfast
- Pork Pie/cakes/biscuits/coffee/tea
- Beer and nibbles
- Evening meal with wine

Visitors are free to join us at any point in these stages and tend to perpetuate supplies.

Happy days indeed.

I have to add that I was particularly proud when my results came back from last week's liver function test.

My consultant said: "Have you been drinking recently?"
I replied: "Yes, I have."
At which he chuckled and said: "Well that explains those then."

COMMENTS (20)

Hi Adrian, no, it doesn't seem strange at all. I was showing my family your blog and explaining how I feel as though I know you and that you are a friend. Never had pen pals as a youngster but perhaps it's along the same lines? Probably more to do with your openness and willingness to share things. Good to hear you're keeping up the relentless socialising - well done for managing to impress your consultant! On a more serious note, it's clear that you are truly living in the 'here and now' - a lesson I have spent much of my 57 years trying to learn and still struggle with. I suspect that I am not alone in that and that you are experiencing a true contentment that is granted to only a few. Long may the good times continue. You and your loved ones are always in my thoughts and prayers. Keep on keeping on my friend. Much love, *Julia xx*

Well I guess everything has an upside and yours is that you don't have to take any notice of the crappy ads about long term liver damage that seem to be on the TV every time I get a glass of chilled chablis out of the fridge. Bums up, make mine a double! Nothing to do with Whitehall or policy is ever fast or simple, my brother works at Westminster and he informed me of this long ago. Keep chipping away at them though, you're getting there. Take care, love *Vicola x*

THE FEAR

July 9, 2008

I sometimes wonder what I put you readers through.

One day it's all guns blazing, drink downing, House of Lords campaigning bravado.

The next day you get this.

Sorry.

On Monday afternoon and evening I was really unwell and was eventually sick.

We are still not sure what caused this but once again it was the uncertainty of being in a situation you don't fully understand or know where it's going to go.

My mum phoned up the excellent district nursing team and I spoke to a sister.

I explained my symptoms then had to run off to vomit while she was still on the line.

The nurses came round really quickly and gave me a strong anti-sickness injection.

The nausea quickly subsided but the drug knocked me out big time.

I felt like Mr T when he made it perfectly clear he wasn't intending to board any plane.

The sedation lasted ALL of Tuesday. I would wake up feeling groggy for about 20 minutes then have to go back to bed for about four hours at least.

I still have a strange feeling in my stomach but it is improving.

As I have written many times before I am not afraid of dying.

However, I am scared that the end stages will be long, drawn-out and unpleasant.

Sedation can really help but that loss of control, which is probably going to happen to me, is frightening.

For all the fun I've been having lately, the decisions I have made, the control I have taken back from this disease; that blip was a timely punch in the head that this situation is unlikely to unfurl in quite the way any of us would hope.

You can forget or kid yourself just how debilitating feeling unwell is.

I always want to be on my feet, out of bed, doing everything I can while I still have time.

Not so exhausted that I have to turn my phone off and leave my friends and family all wondering and worrying.

Lying in bed, not knowing if you are going to get better, or what exactly is causing you to feel sick, is scary.

The times you are awake but unable to function normally are the worst. There is too much time to think seriously about those end stages and with your stomach aching, your body feeling out of sorts, I did find myself getting a bit upset.

You find self-pity rearing its ugly and pointless head again.

My mind opens up again to the injustice and seemingly relentless tragedy that you have all shared over the last 18 months or so.

Please, when my time does run out, let it be as peaceful as possible.

I've had my fair share of unpleasant experiences - as have all my family and friends.

I'm writing this at 5.45am on Wednesday.

That is a good indication that the sedation has worn off and my body clock is desperately trying to readjust. I feel tons better and have a quieter day planned ahead.

COMMENTS (144)

You are a truly amazing man. *Hazel*

Adrian, it is scary. Hard for me to even wrap my head around, so I can't imagine how it must be for you. It isn't fair and I'm sure no one blames you for any amount of self-pity. You have started a chain of events that has wrapped around the world, and we will remain unbroken. Hugs and a good cider (my favourite thing to drink in England! I know, weak, huh?) :) *Gillian, USA*

Glad to know you are feeling better. I can't even begin to imagine how scary all of this must be for you. You sound like you have a wonderful family and a lot of good friends and you are all making some wonderful memories together. Keep up the good fight and stay well. *Sarah*

STOMACH BUG STRIKES

July 13, 2008

It looks more and more likely that a stomach bug of some sort is behind this.

I still think I'm getting better but since last Monday both my parents, my sister and several guests, have all fallen victim to the same sickness and uncomfortable guts.

In most cases these should clear up within a couple of days but I am concerned that for me it's going to take much longer.

If any of the symptoms do get worse I think a trip back into hospital might be a good call - even though it's the last place I want to be.

The symptoms include fatigue, making me even more tired than usual, and having to draw a close on all the festivities this weekend.

That is just annoying.

In better news a push on the campaign has done well. And remember we are aiming to hit 10,000 by July 23.

COMMENTS (24)

Hey… Sorry to hear that you are finally suffering from what us mere mortals have to put up with when we eat a dodgy curry! Seriously, hope you find it a bit of relief to know it's nothing more sinister even if it does take a bit longer to recover from :-) I'm sure you will be partying on soon… I'm still sending out the e-mails, still hoping! *Dawny*

Adrian, sorry to hear a nasty bug got you and your family. Hope you and the medical folks can squash it quickly. Those nasty bacteria and viruses have had thousands/millions of years to devise ways to make animals like us sick and spread their kin. But we humans don't give up easily either. I have faith you will soon find relief and return to enjoying time with those you love and all the festivities! Take care, and don't worry about anything. I am sure your friends are on top of all that needs doing. And from around the world, we are all sending warm thoughts to you, cool ones if you find yourself feverish (we are very perceptive that way). *Margaret, USA*

AN UNEXPECTED BIRTHDAY

July 15, 2008

More gremlins I'm afraid but finally I have been able to finish this post off.

After the 'bad news' I never thought for a second I would see my 27th birthday.

I think I am still living back in May, and time, what with the general fun and now the illness, has just disappeared.

I'm not normally a big fan of birthdays but it would seem daft not to mark this one.

Let's face it, and this is a bit sad to actually write, but it's very likely to be my last.

Despite still feeling poorly my family and I are still going to have a fun day today.

I knew my birthday was looking up when my dad picked up this hugely inappropriate birthday cake. Made us all laugh though.

For many of you who don't know Keith - yes his name is Keith - he only reads books by Bernard Cornwell, preferably the Sharpe ones and loves Carry on Films. Needless to say it was a fine choice.

The comments from all you have been incredible as well. I have asked Liam to actually do some work for a change and get publishing them! We had about 60 in one minute!

Let's start with some good news.

It is my birthday.

The door has not stopped being banged on by postmen and couriers bringing me cards and presents.

It is incredible. Me and my parents have never known anything like it.

A little journalist joke as well. Being 27 now will throw every single hack who covers my story again in the coming weeks and months.

I also know what you are thinking: there is a fine line between sophisticated, fabulous and camp.

I love my dressing gown and it is particularly helpful when I'm breaking out in the sweats. It does look like something Oscar Wilde might have worn and maybe I should crack on with those old-school cigarettes with a holder.

It is from Paul Smith darling and is from my fabulous grandma no less.

Conclusion: camp.

Please note the Lucozade.

The bad news is I still feel unwell.

My stomach is making noises I have never heard before. The volume of the gurgling is deafening.

It seems to start off in my chest and then helter skelter round my stomach and intestines.

I was up at least four times in the night so again I just need to sleep through.

Dehydration is my current biggest battle but I have already knocked back two pints of orange cordial with ice.

I feel unsettled and generally unwell.

The district nurse has just been round and taken blood and I couldn't help temporarily feeling a bit sorry for myself with my lot.

Don't worry - I have bucked my ideas up now.

I don't think there will be any booze today and there won't be excessive eating but I am determined to stay out of hospital.

It's just so difficult having a very limited immune system.

My family and friends, who have all come down with this bug, are making progress.

I seem to be staying the same or, if anything, getting worse.

Thanks again for all the best wishes. The amount of cards and presents, as you can see, has been overwhelming and I really wasn't expecting anything like this.

Thank you to everyone who sent a present or a card or took time to post a comment. There have been nearly 400 in the last 48 hours.

That is a phenomenal and very touching response.

There is also a birthday greeting from the UK's Education Secretary Ed Balls: "On Adrian's birthday I just wanted to renew my pledge that we will do all we can in government to back Adrian's aim to educate all young people on the need for bone marrow donation.

"To this end Alan Johnson and I will be writing to every secondary school to make sure they have the materials and information they need for discussions in school about bone marrow donation.

"You have only to read Adrian's blog to see how passionate he is and how he has a sense of mission about this idea. His campaign has been courageous and inspiring and I will continue to do all I can to back Adrian's mission."

Nice one!

Campaign update in next post with some written answers.

Finally, what are you lot trying to suggest about me?

As soon as this bloody bug goes I will be enjoying some of these lovely bottles I have been sent.

Thanks again and best wishes to you all too.

COMMENTS (340)

Happy Birthday Adrian, and make it woopy! *Annajon*

Hi Adrian. Happy Birthday… I hope you have a great day and make the most of it. I was pleased to hear that you have been allowed out of hospital for this special day. Love and best wishes. *Clare*

Happy birthday dear Adrian. I do hope you have a fantastic day my friend, and continue sticking the proverbial two fingers up at the illness. You are an inspiration. You really have made me put my life and my pitiful "problems" into perspective! You ROCK. Loads of love and stuff to you and yours on your very special day. I can only imagine how proud your family must be of you because without meaning to sound patronising, you make me very, very proud and I don't "know" you really. I'm just one of the thousands that try and walk with you with every post. Take care dear friend. *Tina*

HITTING 10,000, A MASSIVE PORK PIE, STOMACH LATEST AND ONE LAST AWARD

July 19, 2008

The number of signatures backing our campaign crashed through the 10,000 mark this morning.

Thank you for all your efforts. It is amazing how so many people have got behind the cause this week.

Our job is now to ensure if anyone hasn't signed the petition to do so before Wednesday to maximise the support.

Nevertheless, what a great result. I think it's fair to say we are all delighted and really proud of this.

Our petition has only been running for a short period of time and the support for it is nothing short of phenomenal.

Thanks again for all your efforts in pulling this off.

How good is this?

This is my present from the team.

It's a massive birthday pork pie - that is clearly another great result.

For the international and non-Yorkshire readers I hope you are beginning to appreciate just how much of a cultural lynchpin the pork pie is in the Huddersfield region.

They are amazing.

I used to love writing stories about couples who opted for a three-tier pork pie rather than a classic wedding cake.

I promise you readers I am not yanking any of your chains.

You wouldn't believe how much care and craftsmanship goes into these meaty masterpieces. I might have mentioned this before but one of the former UK Prime Ministers came from Huddersfield. When he held office apparently he had pies brought down specifically from the town and had it in Number 10 with HP brown sauce - the only way to have pies so I've been told.

So there you go.

As for my illness and stomach things are still not brilliant.

My stomach remains really unsettled and I just feel uncomfortable in myself.

It's such a shame because it means I don't really want to be around people that much.

I really don't suit being miserable but this illness is doing its best to pull me down.

There clearly is no point to this.

It's an utterly futile and meaningless experience. It's not severe enough to kill me but it is potent enough to stop me from doing all the things I love in life - socialising, eating, drinking and laughing.

Some nights my stomach just gets so bloated that it's like some colossal barrel.

My recent blood test results showed that I hardly have any white blood cells in my body to fight off infections. That would explain why I am struggling so much with such a straight forward tummy bug.

The bacteria fighting wing of your immune system is significantly made up of white blood cells called neutrophils.

Don't worry about the units but to help put my crisis in perspective they were at 0 after my bone marrow transplant and at the Sheffield Hallamshire hospital you are not allowed out of isolation until they creep back up to 1. Mine are around 0.3 now.

The bug is also really infectious so I have to take care not to hug my guests and family.

Being quite tactile I find this difficult.

And finally one last award to report - there can't be any more now!

As many of you know my ambition was always to make it as a science or health reporter on a national newspaper.

I hoped to combine my physiology knowledge from Liverpool University with all the journalistic skills I was picking up in Huddersfield.

Until leukaemia struck it seemed like I needed an opportunity or 'break' but otherwise it was a very attainable goal.

For the international readers the Daily Telegraph is the UK's best selling broadsheet newspaper shifting around a million copies a day.

I wrote, what I thought, was an excellent essay about cutting edge research into obesity.

From a science point of view this is much more what this competition is about.

This year I spotted the award and bashed out 800 words for it.

I emailed it through a couple of months back and thought nothing else of it.

It took me hardly any time but as you can see from the essay below it's not really about new science but it is a striking piece which I imagine caught the judges' eyes.

The judging panel is quite impressive.

It includes Sir David Attenborough - not Richard the actor in Jurassic Park or Gandhi director - but the eminent naturalist and broadcaster.

Needless to say I didn't win anything at university.

Even to be recognised as one of the runner-ups is excellent for me.

Thousands of people enter this competition and before I do die it's further recognition that in some small way I am a national science writer and I do possess the skills of being able to translate complicated medical/scientific issues into language lots of people can engage with and enjoy reading.

For me this means a lot.

For those who are interested here is my essay.

The dark side of bone marrow transplants
By Adrian Sudbury

I should be dead.

Twelve months ago cancer in my bone marrow came within a fortnight of killing me.

Chemotherapy failed and I had no choice but to undergo a bone marrow transplant.

It was a gruelling process both physically and emotionally. I have never felt so unwell and five weeks in an isolation room at Sheffield's Royal Hallamshire hospital was mentally crushing.

Thanks to the generosity of a complete stranger, a 30-year-old woman from Germany, I survived leukaemia.

But that survival came at a price.

Bone marrow is the source of red blood cells, which carry oxygen around the body, and the white blood cells that contribute to our immune systems.

The transplant therefore led to some remarkable changes taking place within me.

Firstly, my O+ blood has now switched to A+, matching that of my donor.

Secondly, and more importantly, my donor's immune system is trying to develop in me.

During a bone marrow transplant drugs are used to turn your immune system off so that the donor's cells are not rejected by the recipient.

Gradually these drugs are tapered down and for about 60% of bone marrow transplant patients they are able to live without daily immunosuppressants.

For the rest, their new immune systems begin to attack their own bodies.

This condition is known as Graft versus Host Disease (GvHD) where the graft refers to the newly 'engrafted' bone marrow cells and the host is the patient.

GvHD can be hugely debilitating and consign some sufferers to wheelchairs.

It can attack the lungs, liver, mouth and gut - proving fatal in some cases.

Sufferers, like me, experience skin problems including; thickening, unrelenting itchiness, reddening, soreness and incredible dryness.

The white blood cells directly involved are called lymphocytes.

Cells in the body are able to distinguish themselves from each other by proteins on their surfaces called antigens.

It's a bit like a uniform. Liver cells carry one type of antigen and skin cells carry another.

Lymphocytes work as part of our immune system by being able to pick out cells with antigens they don't recognise and destroying them.

Usually these are viruses or bacteria but in my case my new lymphocytes don't recognise the antigens associated with my skin.

Different people are affected by GvHD in different ways. In some people their new lymphocytes decide to attack their joints causing them to seize up. In others it dries their eyes out; some people suffer terrible problems with their digestive system.

Significant numbers are never cured and some are unable to ever return to work.

Why all this happens and why it affects different people in such a variety of ways remains a mystery.

What it is about the certain organs I have listed that make them so prone to GvHD is also unknown.

Some treatments are available but for many it is a case of management rather than cure.

The first line of defence is steroids.

They work by blocking the receptors on the surface of the lymphocytes thereby stopping them from acting.

This of course causes problems - the most obvious one being that it massively reduces the ability of your immune system.

Infection is the greatest cause of death for patients with GvHD.

Other long-term problems with high-dose steroid treatment include bloating, weight gain, adrenal disorders, cramps, higher risk of diabetes and mental health problems.

They are not great drugs to be on.

The chance of a long-term cure, or improvement in the condition, is offered by a treatment called Extra Corporeal Photopheresis (ECP).

If it sounds suitably confusing and a tad bizarre then good - because it is!

Twice a month I spend three hours attached to something a bit like a dialysis machine.

A needle is placed in my arm and about half a litre of my blood is taken out.

This is then transferred to a bowl which spins out the white blood cells.

These cells are then mixed with a special chemical that is sensitive to UV light.

This mixture next passes into a chamber that resembles a miniature sunbed.

The UV light activates the chemical which in turn begins to kill the lymphocytes.

Blood, along with the damaged and dying lymphocytes, is then returned to my body.

The idea is that somehow this 'trains' the new immune system to be more tolerant but more research is required in order to fully understand the mechanisms involved.

GvHD is an unpleasant condition but it is important to remember one crucial and ironic fact.

A small amount will actually help fight off any remaining leukaemia.

If it can be managed it represents my best chance of long-term survival.

Ends

I appreciate the irony that this last sentence is now somewhat dated!

COMMENTS (75)

And yet another award! This one I suspect is particularly special though Adrian. So very proud of you, as you should be of yourself. And Sir David Attenborough?! Another pat on your back there Sudders. Impressive panel indeed. Not to make light of your other awards in any way but this award, as you've said, has honoured you as the national science writer that you are! I doubt that there are many more people in the world today who have hundreds if not thousands of lay persons following a blog that is so scientific in its content. The personal touch is what has endeared you to us but, that aside, you have always been able to break the scientific aspect down into layman's terms for us without compromising the actual "scientific-ness" of it all - as you can tell from my latest invented word I am no journalist and certainly not a science writer! We all have a clear understanding of leukaemia, its treatment, the effects and side effects of said treatments, GvHD and of course bone marrow transplants and how they work - and it's only because of your ability to write so succinctly and captivate us all. "If it sounds suitably confusing and a tad bizarre then good - because it is!"… Brilliant! Really sorry to hear your tummy's still giving you beans. If there was any way I could help improve your quality of life I would. You're in my thoughts always and I wish for you, daily, that you are able to enjoy your time with your family and friends! Sending warm thoughts, tight hugs and soothing kisses your way - with no fear of catching your illness from all the way across the pond in Trinidad - so be as tactile as you wish and hug back tight. *Tash*

Hi Adrian, sorry to hear that you are still having problems with your stomach. One more award, are you sure there will be no more awards? I think there will be more to come! Difficult to read your blog without crying. Now I have finished reading the whole thing. Sometimes I think I shouldn't have read this because it makes me sooo sad. But the good thing is you changed me a lot, now I know the importance of life, before I never thought seriously about life. Now with what little time we all spend in this world, we must do whatever we can for the betterment of fellow human beings. Have a nice weekend Adrian. *Shiney from India.*

SUDDERS, AND THE CAMPAIGN DREAM TEAM, DO NUMBER 10 DOWNING STREET - UPDATING THROUGHOUT THE DAY
July 22, 2008

Hello again everyone.

Right, I thought we could have some fun with this one.

We have got a petition to hand in at Downing Street and I thought you could all come along with us.

It's now 8.45pm on Tuesday and the plan is to be there around 12pm tomorrow.

So rather than just write about it I thought we could post live hourly updates throughout the day and try and stick some pictures in as we go along too.

Might be a bit rough round the edges but this is probably going to be the last big outing I make so why not make the most of it?

First of all just a little update on my health.

Thank you to everyone who has asked.

I am shattered. My energy levels are terrible and every time my stomach seems to be improving it just kicks off again.

Managed to get out in my car this weekend and had one last night in my Sheffield flat.

It was a wonderful sense of independence again.

I'm really pleased I got to say goodbye to my home in High Green - I loved that place - but there was a strange mixture of happy memories tainted with unrelenting tragedy.

Not many humans go so quickly from planning their own wedding to planning their own funeral. More on that in a future post.

As for this morning I just felt really sick.

I got the car back to my parents, then crashed out and slept for much of the afternoon.

Hoping to save up some energy for tomorrow.

Tuesday - 10pm Examiner reporter Katie Campling arrives at the media hub (my parents' house) and my mum feeds her. Spend time discussing tomorrow. Looks like train is at 9am from Derby.

We were going to be picked up in a ministerial car from St Pancras station but now it looks like it's going to be super Kali Mountford MP's Ford Mondeo - live the dream!

Spent time letting all the media people know about it. This has been a bit short notice but both really looking forward to it.

Hoping our petition can creep up into 6th place in the country as the day progresses. The actual closing time is midnight we think.

Time for sleep.

Wednesday - 6.30am. Sort of wake up. Really tired but know if I fall back to sleep it will be even harder to get going. Fire up the computer and great to see so many of you commenting. Thanks very much. Stomach not great but so far so good. Going to try some breakfast.

Wednesday - 8.10am. Off in the car to Derby Station. Beanie hat and suit donned. Absolutely exhausted!

Hoping to rest up in car and train.

Petition latest: 10,678

Wednesday - 8:52am. **Hi it's Liam here,** I will be helping update the blog whilst our friend Adrian is out and about. This means whilst he is out having an adventure I'll be sitting in here typing away on a computer. I'm kind of like Alfred the Butler, to Adrian's Batman.

Petition just jumped up to: 10,684

Wednesday - 9:04am. Train from Derby as seen above. Mum and Dad weren't sure what to get me for my birthday, so they decided to upgrade me to 1st class, really kind of them. Apologies for the picture. This update is for my little friend Ryan Patrick, from the USA. He's a bit poorly at the moment and he loves trains like me! These are the big intercity trains that travels from the North to South of England. Get well Soon!

Tune into Radio 5 Live at 11:30am they're covering this story.

Wednesday - 10.30am. First Class baby. Living the dream on steroids and Red Bull. Next stop St Pancras, London. I am starting to pick up a bit now.

Radio 5 Live are going to call my moblie at 11.30am. Katie and I have now arranged to meet the local TV news, channel5 news and the Press Association outside number 10. Phones haven't stopped ringing all morning. Good fun though.

Petition update: 10,717 - Let's keep going.

Wednesday - 11:06am. Slight change of plans. Had to hop in a cab. Heading towards House of Commons will rendezvous with Kali, the rest of the team and the Mondeo at St Stephen's entrance.

Petition update: 10,724 - Looking good

Wednesday - 11:42am. **Liam:** Adrian is a bit busy at the moment, by my calculations he should be getting interviewed now. I'm waiting on an update from him hopefully some of you have been able to listen to him or his story on Radio 5 Live.

Wednesday - 12:06pm. We are here. Pimp my Mondeo.

Wednesday - 1:35pm. **Liam:** I've just had a phone call from Adrian. Things are going really well, he's a bit tired but in his own words "doing plenty of media whoring". He's just having a bit of lunch and will be sending us some updates shortly.

Wednesday - 2:27pm. Some more updates from Adrian. They have only just arrived, so seem a little out of sequence but here they are.

Wednesday - 11:45am. Jeremy Clarkson will kill me. On closer inspection it's not a Mondeo; actually it's a Ghia. Or is it a Mondeo, Ghia? Still loving it though.

Randomly bumped into Ed Balls at Westminster. He said: "I'm supposed to be seeing you in five minutes!" Finished 5live interview and headed over to Downing Street.

Wednesday - Noon. Arrive at Downing Street. Great feeling driving through the gates. Big Grandma and friend Jamie cheering us on as gates opened up. Small media circus awaited us too. Felt like a Z list celebrity. Ed Balls running a bit late so had lots of opportunity to have pictures taken, speak to the media and do filming.

Wednesday - 12:15pm. Enter Number 10 Downing Street and meet with Ed Balls in one of the many rooms. Hand over petition. Really good meeting. Very receptive as ever. Discussed the difficulties in making it compulsory for colleges: nevertheless, he said the government was determined to do all it could to back the campaign and make it an annual feature. Chatted for about 15 min. Stomach just about behaving but getting very hot and run down. Given a really interesting tour of number 10. Saw the famous staircase with the portraits of all the Prime Ministers on.

Wednesday - 1:00pm. Back outside, completed round of media interviews. Lots of interest. Out on Yorkshire news, Channel 5 news and hopefully Sky news as well tonight. Drive back over to Westminster for lunch with the campaign dream team, Kali, Katie, Caroline and Ian.

Wednesday - 2:30pm. Finishing lunch and heading over to complete last media interview. Getting increasingly tired. Looking forward to bed later.

Petition update: 10,849 - we've just overtaken the campaign to "ensure there is a Lasting Legacy for Shooting Sports in the UK by moving the venue away from the Woolwich Barracks".

Wednesday - 4.30pm. Say goodbye to Kali Mountford and Ian at Westminster. Jump in a taxi and head back to St Pancras. Hop on the train back to Derby and just relaxing with a glass of red wine.

Katie is writing her report for The Huddersfield Examiner. I am shattered and really looking forward to a good lie down. It has been an excellent day and I have enjoyed every minute of it. I really hope all this work will make a lasting difference. Train due back into Derby at 5.56pm

Wednesday - 5:14pm. At this time the petition stands at 10,977 which is a fantastic result. Adrian is really happy with how things have gone. Thank you everyone who has signed the petition. If you think today was exciting tune in tomorrow. We will be playing Adrian's Desert Island discs from BBC Sheffield. It's going to be a great post.

Wednesday - 10.30pm. What a brilliant day. Got home around 6.30pm and had tea with Katie and another really good friend Sian. My parents told me how proud they were of me too.

In bed just reading through all your wonderful comments and wanted to say how much fun writing today's post has been.

I think we have really embraced the multi-media format well and thanks for all sharing such a great day out.

Special thanks to Liam who has really worked hard today on this - despite trying to do his normal duties. My parents for the lifts, feeding and taking notes over the phone to file through to Liam.

Also a huge shout out to Katie Campling for all her efforts behind the scenes. The same goes to Caroline Berger of the Anthony Nolan Trust but most of all Kali Mountford MP and her office manager Ian Leedham who have put so much time and energy into pulling all this off.

Thank you to you all and for making this day possible.

COMMENTS (225)

Hi Adrian, good to hear from you, and sorry your tum is still playing up. I hope you make the national news tomorrow evening with your visit to Downing Street. Good luck with that and look forward to seeing any pics. I am going away for a week very shortly, so won't be able to keep up with your news. If you are having more jungle juice on Friday I hope you will have more energy to enjoy the weekend. It must have been a good feeling to drive your car and spend one more night in your flat. Well sweet cheeks I send my love, as usual, to you and your family. I hope tomorrow won't be too tiring for you, but just think what you have achieved. Over ten and a half thousand signatures in such a short time. You are a wonderful person Adrian and we are all so proud of you. Stay strong. Bless you. *Ree*

I'm doing a late shift tomorrow, lots of colleagues are off sick, no way I can go to London. I work with adults with learning disabilities, you see, they rely on me. I hope you have a fantastic day and get to meet lots of people from here. I'll check the blog when I get home at 10 pm. It's good to hear from you! :) *TAFKAI (The Alexandra Formerly Known As Italic)*

Fab to hear you are going to muster the energy to get to Downing St… If I can get away from work in time, I will deffo be there… Hoping that you find some consolation in that you are getting time to say farewell to the things you hold dear… Stay strong my friend. *xxxreiki hugsxxxx*

MORNING AFTER THE DAY BEFORE

July 24, 2008

Liam: Thank you for all your support yesterday, the final numbers for the petition were 11,301. A fantastic result.

I've had an email from Adrian's mum today. Unfortunately Adrian was sick last night and had to call on the services of the excellent sister from the District Nursing team who came straight out and gave him an injection to help the nausea. She gave him a lower dose than the one which zonked him out a few weeks ago and so he has been able to get some sleep without being absolutely knocked out, but is very groggy all the same. He is not too well today, understandably after all his hard work yesterday.

However he spent ages last night reading all the comments on the blog and was thrilled that everyone enjoyed the visit with him. He is always touched by what people take the time to write and yesterday was no exception

HATE THIS

July 25, 2008

Woken up today just feeling unutterably sorry for myself and generally terrible.

Was able to sleep for hours yesterday and really thought I would be brightening up this morning.

Well the stomach discomfort has started again and I think that's why I was woken up at 6am rather than any natural causes.

I have to have a day in hospital anyway on Friday for blood.

Feeling unsettled aside I am exhausted because I need red blood cells and my arms and legs are starting to shake a little.

Why do I have to put up with this?

Pain is one thing - but I've been ill for three weeks.

No one seems to be able to do anything for me.

As soon as it kicks off my quality of life disappears. I don't want anyone around me, I just want to curl up in a drain somewhere and die.

I'm sick of hanging on.

I just know this is going to take ages to conclude and I have had enough.

MOVING INTO THE CLOSING STAGES

July 26, 2008

I think some of you will find this post hard, others will find it positive; I think most of you will find it sad.

My life expectancy literally is weeks now.

I know we have been saying that for a while but my white cell count is spiralling upwards and out of control.

After Friday's rather miserable post I have to say I am actually feeling OK.

I spoke to my consultant while having blood and basically asked: "What is the point of this?"

Think about it, what is the point of carrying on with this half-existence? I can't eat much, have a beer, socialising with friends is difficult if my stomach is ripping into me. I'm weak and progressively deteriorating.

Why draw this period out?

I have tied up lots of loose ends including my will, bank accounts, arranging gifts/letters for loved ones.

We have achieved all we can for the time being with the campaign.

All I need is a bit more time to tie up one or two more loose ends.

I asked my consultant what he felt was his aim for life expectancy on this management regime and he said the end of summer early autumn.

I replied I didn't want to go on like this for that period of time and asked about my options.

Basically he said if I decided to come off all my tablets it would bring that life expectancy down from say six weeks to two or three.

For me, that was an easy call to make.

So on Monday my family and I are meeting up with my excellent GP, district nursing and Macmillan nursing teams, to discuss a plan of action while I am still sound of mind.

It helps me take some control back over this unenviable position I find myself.

The consultant even thought I might not make the following Friday.

I laughed and said: "No, way, Sudburys are as tough as old boots." So we had a gentleman's wager!

This might sound morbid but if I was you I would be wondering about how I'm going to die.

Assuming an infection doesn't clobber me first it will actually be a consequence of the leukaemia.

There are many different white blood cells in the body which usually help fight off infection.

You will have probably heard of 'high white cell counts' in association with this blood cancer.

As the cancer in the bone marrow spreads and takes up more room, more and more of these cells are 'squeezed' out, into the blood stream.

The consequence of this is the blood gets sludgier and more viscous.

This then starts to impair organ function. The consultant explained that I will start to feel more tired and less alert as this takes place in the brain.

That is definitely already beginning.

It sounds horrific but I've been assured that dying from leukaemia isn't necessarily painful. The district nurses will be increasingly on hand to help out and towards the end apparently many patients just fall asleep.

I really hope that is true in my case.

One of my biggest sources of anxiety though was how I was going to sort out visits from all my friends?

There are lots of people who want to see me to say goodbye and I was really getting myself worked up about this. I do not possess the energy to be rounding up and co-ordinating people from all over the country.

Thankfully, after one phone call from my dad, my friends have all pulled together, agreed a timetable of short visits and agreed not to come if I am feeling awful.

Shows you just how good my friends are.

Can't remember if I posted this either but we are planning on having two funeral services.

The first will be a really private and intimate affair at a local church.

The second will be open to absolutely anyone at Sheffield Cathedral.

Dates and time will be published on the blog.

Planning both (bearing in mind I was planning my wedding four months ago) was initially heartbreaking and my parents and I both cried.

After that initial upset though the process was genuinely cathartic and we all started laughing and thinking about beautiful music, prayers, readings and hymns that would be appropriate.

It's not been easy but I'm glad I had the opportunity to share something like that with parents I love so much.

My stomach has been better today.

I tried some laxative and it has helped move things through and decrease the pressure.

Obviously there are consequences but at least I'm less miserable!

COMMENTS (401)

Adrian. Well, what can anyone say to your post. Obviously we all know the inevitable was going to happen, but the fact that we may only have another couple of weeks with you is breaking my heart. The way you and your family are coping with this is unbelievable. Being a Nottingham Panthers fan I'm a bit dubious about venturing into Sheffield but for you Adrian, I'll be there. Take care for now. Love as always, *Lisa x*

Adrian, at this point my wish for you is peace. You are a very brave person who has made a difference for so many today and so many in the future. Although this was very hard for me to read I think about you often and wonder how you are. My thoughts and prayers are with you. Do what is best for you. *Cheryl*

DESERT ISLAND SUDDERS
July 28, 2008

Sometimes I'm so glad I started this blog.

There have been some good times; I say that but on reflection they have been mainly bad.

But nevertheless, my illness and what I've decided to do with it, has undeniably led to some interesting places.

I think you are really going to enjoy this post because it's so different to anything I have done before.

Basically, through Radio Sheffield, I was offered the opportunity to take part in a Desert Island Discs-style show.

In the UK we have this famous Radio 4 programme where the scenario is as follows. If you were to crash on a Desert Island which tracks would you take with you and why.

I've always thought I'd love to do it and when asked to pick my six I jumped at the chance.

It is actually quite difficult to choose so maybe some of you could post your top six too - just to get a flavour of what some of you like out there.

It's an interesting show and has revealed the music likes of top politicians, artists and general eminent figures for the last 40 or so years.

It all came about through this guy Toby Foster.

He presents the breakfast show in Sheffield and is a top bloke.

He is a well-known and successful comedian in and around Sheffield and is one of those characters who pops up randomly on TV from time to time.

For example, he starred in Phoenix Nights as Les the Drummer and the token northern comic in the Christmas special of Extras.

I've met lots of presenters but Toby really made an impression.

Bearing in mind the breakfast show people are often the ones with the biggest egos he could not have been more genuine and supportive.

After my first time on the show he actually read the blog and took time to post a comment.

He is the only presenter who has actually bothered to do this.

When I talk to taxi drivers in town too they always seem to like him as well.

You can always trust a cabbie to be a good judge of character!

I was asked back into the studio when I was told I only had weeks or months to live and we were really rushed.

Afterwards, he asks if I would like to come back in tomorrow and record a one-off special.

If you are objective about it, and when I put my journalist hat on, it is a really good story.

The idea was I'd go home, pick my six favourite tracks, then do a pre-recorded show the following morning.

I loved the idea.

Now without getting too weird Radio Sheffield will probably play this in full when I pop the old clogs - well, it will fill an hour on a bank holiday or something.

But, it's great they have let us use it here because obviously many of you would not have the opportunity to check it out.

What really makes me laugh about Desert Island discs is when they have on politicians or intellectuals.

Their choices are so blatantly determined by the persona they wish to portray - or their spin doctors believe they should be portraying.

David Cameron, Conservative leader, had Fake Plastic Trees by Radiohead as one of his songs.

Regular blog readers will have spotted that I love Radiohead and maybe he does too, maybe he does.

But I just can't see Mr Cameron cruising around in his Toyota Prius listening to The Bends or Kid A.

Dave - please write in and tell me otherwise.

The other lot are in some ways even worse.

Several pieces of really obscure classical music? "Oh yes, I simply adore this exquisite part of the third movement of Bach's Partita Number 3."

Shut up.

Bang on PJ and Duncan's Let's Get Ready to Rumble and have done with it you pretentious nob.

I hope my choices are an accurate reflection of me.

One final point.

Obviously I'm really keen to share the music with you. We do actually have permission to use Brianstorm because I was hoping to round the blog off to that and asked their management.

Using other tracks gets us bogged down in all sorts of copyright issues. As a work around I really hope the big music companies won't mind us linking through to the tracks on YouTube. They have been on there for ages and look, have a heart, I am dying from leukaemia.

If there is a problem please just get in touch with us first and we will happily remove the links.

COMMENTS (229)

Great post - I'm glad that you were allowed to share it with us! Funny... I heard about Desert Island Discs for the very first time yesterday in a book that I was reading. We've always played the game here in Canada, but I didn't realise that anyone had ever made an actual show out of it. Cool! *Jen*

Sounds a great idea. Can't wait to hear all your choices, I don't know how you managed to pick six songs out in a day. An impossible task! Off the top of my head I'd have: 'Street Spirit' by Radiohead, 'No Rain' by Blind Melon, 'Elderly Woman Behind the Counter in a Small Town' by Peal Jam, 'Bullet with Butterfly Wings' by Smashing Pumpkins, 'Debaser' by Pixies and... of course 'Let's Get Ready to Rumble' by PJ and Duncan. I'll let you know if I change my mind overnight! *xxxx Cath*

Not wanting to make you jealous Adrian but 'The One and Only' Chesney Hawkes performed at my Graduation Ball. I even copped a feel of him! haha *xx Cath*

Wow six tracks, it's really hard! 1. Blower's daughter by Damien Rice. 2. Advertising space by Robbie Williams. 3. Porcelain by Moby. 4. Mad World by Gary Jules. 5. Perfect by Vanessa Amerossi. 6. Bedshaped by Keane. *Barb, Melbourne*

Top six though would have to be: Linkin Park - Numb, Black Sabbath - Paranoid, Alison Moyet - All Cried Out, David Bowie - Rebel Rebel, Genesis - In Too Deep, Paul Young - Wherever I Lay my Hat. Also agree Chesney Hawkes and One and Only - bit of a legend. *Sally*

Fantasia on a Theme by Thomas Tallis - R Vaughan Williams, The Passenger - Iggy Pop, Too Lost in You - Sugababes, The Division Bell - Pink Floyd, Constant Craving - kd lang. I want to dedicate this last one to you: My Hero - Foo Fighters. *Amanda*

FUTURE OF ADRIAN'S ARMY
August 1, 2008

Liam: Quick update first of all to keep you informed. Adrian's mum has told me that, "Adrian is at the hospital at the moment for a routine transfusion of blood and platelets. He is very tired but not too uncomfortable and in good spirits."

He is also trying to spend as much time as possible seeing all of his friends and family with all the time he has left. As soon as I hear any updates I will let you all know.

One of the things Adrian is very interested about, is for "Adrian's Army" - that is you his readers - to keep in contact with each other in the future. So I am looking for suggestions as to how we can best do this.

Obviously to start off we have this blog, and I hope in the future that we can continue updating the blog with news and updates - about Adrian's campaign, bone marrow donation and similar news. This is something Adrian has asked me to do, and I would like to see the blog last as Adrian's legacy. But just as important is keeping the wonderful community on this blog, and I would like to hear your thoughts and suggestions about this. Adrian has always thought one of the best things about his blog has been his readers. Your kind wishes and support have given him real strength over these difficult times, and I would really like to say thank you for this.

One of our commenters Bethany has contacted me and suggested we create a widget that could be posted on other blogs and social networks.

Do you think this is a good idea, and what would you suggest that the widget does?

Do you think we should creating a mailing list, whereby people could sign up to receive updates and information to their email accounts? Would you sign up for such a list, and how would you like to see it used?

Do you use social networks such as Facebook, and would you sign up to an Adrian's Army group? If so what do you think the group should do and contain?

If you have any thoughts but do not want to post them as a reply to this post, please email me direct liam.mcneilis@liverpool.com

COMMENTS (144)

I think this is a wonderful idea. A touching legacy for a brave young man and an ongoing fight for a cure. *Nicky*

I would certainly sign up to a mailing list and also join a facebook group. Thanks Liam, for the update on Adrian. He is always in my thoughts. *CJD*

PRINCE CHARLES PRAYING FOR ME AND SUPPORT FROM BORIS JOHNSON
August 3, 2008

As you know now I am increasingly dropping out of it.

My colleagues did remind me about my letters from Prince Charles and London Mayor Boris Johnson but it wasn't until I spotted comments from Tash and Katherine that I thought I should really include them in the blog.

Many thanks for reminders.

Was sick last night again but generally had a better day today.

Prince Charles is praying for Adrian
by Katie Campling, Huddersfield Daily Examiner

The Prince of Wales has said he is praying for campaigning leukaemia sufferer Adrian Sudbury.

Prince Charles said he hopes Adrian's "spirited fight" to educate more people about bone marrow donation is a success.

The future king's comments came in a letter from his official residence, Clarence House, in response to the Examiner's request for him to support our Sign Up For Sudders campaign.

The campaign was started three months ago by Examiner journalist Adrian, 27, when he discovered the leukaemia he was suffering from was terminal.

He decided to spend his last few weeks raising awareness about the need for more donors to sign up to the bone marrow register and give a chance to the 16,000 people in the world who need a transplant to live.

Adrian has also waged a high-level campaign with the Government to ensure all 17 and 18-year-olds are educated as standard about donation.

The Examiner wrote to Prince Charles to see if he would lend his personal support to Adrian's campaign and also what scope there would be for his Prince's Trust charity to become involved.

While the prince cannot directly support the campaign he said his Prince's Foundation for Integrated Health may be able to assist.

The Clarence House letter said: "His Royal Highness is grateful to you for taking the trouble to let him know about this inspirational young man and the campaign.

"The Prince of Wales hopes that your campaign is a great success and will pray for Adrian as he continues his battle."

Adrian's efforts have also attracted praise from London Mayor Boris Johnson.

The Examiner originally contacted Mr Johnson's office to see if they would circulate a link to our online petition on the Downing Street website.

The petition, which closed on July 23 with 11,301 signatures, called on the Government to ensure better education about donation as standard in UK schools and colleges.

Mr Johnson said: "Adrian Sudbury is a courageous man who has conducted an amazing bone marrow donation awareness campaign while battling his own cancer.

"Adrian's positive work has helped dispel the myths about donating bone marrow, which will help save thousands of lives."

COMMENTS (145)

Incredible! That's great Adrian. You should be very proud. *Bethany*

Wow, Royalty bowing to Our Adrian- Quite right too! *Christine M*

How does it feel to dream of the queen one night and then hear from Prince Charles just about the next day? *Liz*

FACEBOOK GROUP & BLOG CHANGES
August 5, 2008

Liam: First and most importantly I've just been on the phone with Adrian. He tells me, he's feeling about the same as when he created the anxiety post but that's not going to stop him working on this blog. Let's face it the man is a tiger.

Just dropping you a minor update about the future of the blog.

Very shortly the blog will be getting a slight redesign, allowing us to re-organise some of the content to make it easier to find, do a few things better. But don't worry all of Adrian's posts and all your comments will stay the same.

I have no fixed time when this will happen and there will be warnings before it does.

Also I have created a group in Facebook for "Adrian's Army" to allow those who use Facebook to keep in contact.

If you search within Facebook for "Adrian's Army - Baldy's Blog" you should be able to find it. It is still in the very early stages, so any help or suggestions would be greatly appreciated.

For those who don't use it - Facebook is a social network. This means it allows people to keep in contact with each other or meet new friends through a website. Similar to Adrian's blog. If that is not something you're interested in, please don't worry as this blog will still be here.

I am still looking into MySpace, mailing lists and a widget, and will keep you updated

CALLING ON ADRIAN'S ARMY
August 6, 2008

Liam: Quick thank you for all the people who have contacted me about Adrian's Army, and have already joined the Facebook group. Got a small task for everyone.

I've been contacted by the Anthony Nolan Trust - and want to draw everyone's attention to a campaign they've set up to show your support for Adrian. Please visit www.anthonynolan.org.uk/media/campaigns/showyoursupportforadrian.htm to find out more about how you personally can support Adrian's campaign to raise awareness of the need for Bone Marrow Donors.

You can make a real difference and help a lot of people so get cracking! Now please be aware this is a UK based list, and I would love to hear from similar groups around the world.

I think Adrian's blog is an incredible testament to how receiving warm wishes at a difficult time can be a great comfort. If you'd like to write a short message of support visit - www.anthonynolan.org.uk/showyoursupportforapatient. The Anthony Nolan Trust will make sure that families affected by leukaemia and other life-threatening conditions will see it. They may also include your message in our online patient support wall.

To see a list of current Donor Recruitment clinics please visit www.anthonynolan.org.uk/donatinglist-of-current-donor-recruitment-clinics.htm and for more information about the process of joining the register please visit www.anthonynolan.org.uk/donating/how-to-join-the-register.htm.

The Anthony Nolan Trust takes back lives from leukaemia by managing, and recruiting new donors to the UK's most successful bone marrow register. The Anthony Nolan Trust is an independent charity (Reg. No. 803716 / SCO38827) and continually relies on support from individuals and companies. Find out how at www.anthonynolan.org.uk

ANXIETY
August 7, 2008

This is a strange and difficult time for me. I have always worried about silly things and of course so much about those I care for.

With the news that it really is a case of a matter of weeks (I'm still not confident about these doctors' predictions) I was crippled with the anxiety about how I am going to see all my family and friends for a good length of time, and make it so they felt like they had every opportunity to say to me precisely what they wanted.

On Saturday, at around 3am, I sat bolt upright.

There was no reason other than I could not get the Queen (Elizabeth II) out of my head. I had this overwhelming sense of panic and deep breathing. It was so strange.

She wasn't doing anything, threatening me with a wedgie or a Chinese burn, I just couldn't shake off the panic.

I went in to see my parents and explained how I was feeling - left out the Queen bit initially.

My dad called the district nurses out and they injected me with a strong sedative which got me back to sleep within about ten minutes.

At that stage I decided the source of the anxiety was a number of factors. Of course the obvious one about a drawn-out death still worries the hell out of me.

I explained in the previous post how my friends stepped in. It doesn't sound very cool to have a timetable but we did and it worked really well.

Over three days I saw around 32 people.

I still wake up at exactly 2am or between 3am and 4am. The nurses always come out and my family, as ever, try and make the most of it.

I was so proud of myself because now everyone has had the opportunity to say goodbye properly.

I feel like I have said everything too and if I died tomorrow, it would be sad, but there would be no regrets.

On the last couple of slots on Thursday afternoon I had to keep pacing up and down the room to stop myself from falling asleep.

I was also given an anti-sickness jab while chatting to Nel Bilton. Poor girl, she is the one who saw blood gushing from my shin after I had fallen in the pond wearing a hideous pair of bright blue boxer shorts.

Now things have switched round and I'm going to put myself and my family at the centre of all this.

The blog is getting harder to write and my focus is waning but it will keep going as best I can.

I think my mum and Liam will be able to keep things moving on when necessary.

How do we all keep in touch?

Thanks for all the interesting feedback about how you can keep in touch after I shuffle off.

We are going to complete our mission!

There seems to be a lot of love for one massive Facebook group, which could be linked to all the smaller sites.

A lot of love is also being shown for a mailing list.

Would people generally go along with this?

I think any more than two, or possibly three, would be duplicating matters.

I must admit I don't know enough about all this and would like to lead the project, but I won't be able to do it.

I think in this post, make it the last chance to express your views. We need something simple anyone can use.

Anyone know of some very simple generic mailing lists websites we we could help ourselves?

When all the quotes stop coming in the geniuses in Liverpool Liam and Steve Harrison can look at making this a reality.

Thanks again everyone.

COMMENTS (82)

Thank you for taking the time to post that, it means the world to your army. Hope you and your loved ones continue to enjoy this precious time and that their love for you will assuage your anxieties. *Cheryl*

Watched Kung Fu Panda and came away with a lovely quote: "Yesterday is history, tomorrow is a mystery but today is a gift - that's why it's called the present." *R*

FACEBOOK ARMY AND A FEW MORE CHALLENGES
August 12, 2008

These last few weeks, or however many, seem to keep unfurling ahead of me, are dotted with incidents of dropping off to sleep, random drowsiness, disorientation and distraction.

Writing this blog is something I still love but it is becoming increasingly challenging to construct.

The latest update is I've been given a syringe driver. This means drugs are constantly put into my body throughout the day. This is why I'm so drowsy and when talking to people, it makes it really difficult to concentrate on what some people are saying.

I appreciate this is something which we have all experienced plenty of at some time in our lives.

I'm on a mixture of painkillers, anti-anxiety and anti-sickness drugs.

It's important that much of my time now is spent with myself and my family rooted at the centre.

My friends all appreciate that, but still want to see me nonetheless and when that can be arranged I will make every effort to make that possible.

In the night, I have a full time nurse from 10pm through to 7am. Should I start to feel sick or unable to fall asleep due to anxiety, they are there to immediately administer an injection.

But over all, quality of life continues to deteriorate. Walking up the stairs is difficult as is picking things up with my right hand.

Again, my parents have been excellent throughout... constant love and an iced drink, day or night.

Facebook

Thank you so much for joining Facebook and keeping in touch with the campaign. I believe that this is going to be a really effective way of you all keeping in touch. This is going to be a long term project. I'm not a Facebook member, but I understand my international friends can sign up to this one.

COMMENTS (118)

I have never commented before Adrian, but read your blog every day. I pray for you every night that you will be comfortable. You are certainly going to leave your mark in this world. Keep strong and God bless. *Sandie*

I was thrilled when I saw that you had taken the time to update! Just wanted to let you know that I'm constantly thinking of you and sending many positive thoughts your way. Glad to hear that you have a helpful nurse with you throughout the night, and that you've been able to spend lots of time with your family. Indeed, that is a top priority. You have been and will continue to be in my prayers! *Valerie*

I WILL PUT YOU THROUGH TO GORDON BROWN NOW...

August 13, 2008

I have just got off the phone with our Prime Minister.

He phoned to explain that he had personally written to all the celebrities that me and the Anthony Nolan Trust had come up with to to try and make people think again about bone marrow donation. He also had nothing but praise for me, the work we have all been doing and he reiterated the fact he thought I was an inspiration. Remember, I had thought of this before but decided not to make it part of the campaign because I just assumed it would be an outright no.

This was very much their idea and the very fact that Mr Brown has phoned me himself to confirm he has written those letters is testament to how much this means to him.

Directly afterwards I was able to speak to Ed Balls again. He also said how inspirational the campaign had been and took his hat off to just how much we have achieved in such a short space of time. We agreed the best way to make this talk possible was to work not only from the top down but from the bottom up too.

I'd like this Government to do as much as it can; produce all the resources to enable the talk to be given.

COMMENTS

Mr Brown is saying what we've all thought for ages... that you're an inspiring man and that this was a brilliant idea. *Lesley*

Hope you kept him on hold for a moment or two - I mean, surely he can't have simply assumed that our mega, international journalist/superhero/superstar would be sitting around in his boxers wrapped in his camp night gown twiddling his thumbs - there are, after all, lives to be saved, souls to inspire, people to unite. Proudest of hugs from Trinidad. *Tash*

ADRIAN PASSES AWAY

August 20, 2008

It's Liam here, I am sorry to be writing the post I never wanted to write. I was sent this email by Adrian's dad Keith Sudbury:

Adrian Sudbury died peacefully in his sleep with his dad Keith and mum Kay last night.

Keith said: "Every parent thinks their son or daughter is special and we are no different.

"Adrian touched all who knew him. We're very proud of all his achievements in tragically such a short time.

"Kay and I hope that all Adrian's good work will be continued by all those who knew and loved him."

There will be a private family funeral followed by a service of remembrance at Sheffield Cathedral at a date to be confirmed.

I'm sure you will all join me in offering your condolences to Adrian's family and friends at this very difficult time.

COMMENTS (429)

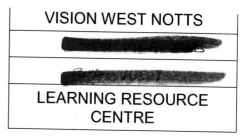